PROJECT

TEAM

DATE

Emergent Futures Lab Press
emergentfutureslab.com

THE INNOVATION DESIGN WORKBOOK - STUDENT EDITION PART 2
First Edition:
Summer 2021 Prototype Edition
Designed by Marco de Mel Pedersen

Iain Kerr and Jason Frasca

NOTE: You have in your possession a working draft printed
for research and development purposes. It is not intended
for general distribution. It is incomplete, contains errors and
missing citations. We really appreciate your use and welcome
any and all feedback. Thank you!

THE INNOVATION DESIGN WORKBOOK

STUDENT EDITION

PART TWO: WORKBOOK

iain kerr and jason frasca

begin anywhere, no ideas but in making

CONTENTS

USING THIS BOOK

We have named the set of tools and procedures that we outline in this book *The Innovation Design Approach*
(or IDA for short). IDA is a way of approaching creativity, invention/innovation and design in general. It is an ethos, an overarching framework and a set of connected practices for producing truly novel outcomes.

It is intended to be pragmatic and applicable across a wide variety of fields from ecology to entrepreneurship, from philosophy to politics, and from basic education to advanced biology. The core focus of the Innovation Design Approach is to help you develop processes that allow for genuinely novel possibilities to emerge in the face of difficult and open-ended areas of interest.

At the heart of our ethos is our conviction that ideas only come about from doing. Reading and ideating alone do not lead to novelty. Thus, we have written a workbook and not a textbook.

For creativity to happen this book needs to be used and not simply read, and it is with this in mind that we invite you to see the purpose of this workbook as being twofold:

1. To help and teach you the key skills and tools for innovation (where our techniques act like a temporary scaffolding); and...

2. To support your unique innovation process no matter what phase of the process you are in.

A couple of additional thoughts:

1. As a learning tool this book is best thought of as a form of scaffolding designed to support and catalyze your learning, and because of this we do not attempt to cover every aspect or every skill needed for innovation. Our goal with this workbook is to give you a sense of the terrain and teach you a set of critical techniques and processes. Ultimately, as your skills develop the scaffolding is left behind.

2. Whatever stage of innovation you are in, we designed this workbook to help you. None of us are starting in the same place or facing the same issues. After the introduction we have a guide: How to Hack the Innovation Process, to help you figure out where to start in this workbook and how to proceed.

3. *On being practical & creative:* our goal is to assist you in experimenting collectively with the real so that the genuinely new emerges. As such our approach is entirely pragmatic. Why does this matter when redefining creativity? Being pragmatic, for us, means that all of our various claims and propositions about creativity and innovation are not intended as the ultimate definitions or final truths on the subject — but as useful tools and lures towards an experimentation that "excludes nothing" as William James puts it. Our goal is creative actions.

That said — pragmatism is never simple — in fact in regards to creativity pragmatism needs to be skeptical of the desire for simplicity. Things are just too surprising. The philosopher who coined the term creativity, A. N. Whitehead puts it well: *seek simplicity and doubt it.*

It's not that we want to make things complicated — far from it, but *change is never simple* -- it is always deeply strange and truly confounding. The pragmatism we are espousing is one of falling in love with change such that radical surprise becomes a given — *wonderment.* Being pragmatic in regards to creativity is to embrace the beauty and a joy of aberrant leaps and qualitative shifts. For us being practical and creative means that we need to care for beauty, joy and strangeness that is fully part of the practice of change.

For us, the Innovation Design Approach is part of an experiment to develop better tools and frameworks
for innovation. As such, this book is an open toolkit which we hope you will experiment and *hack* freely.
This framework's utility can be judged by whether it works for you.

How will you know if it works? Try the practices, do they lead you somewhere interesting? In doing so, we hope that you will change these practices and make them your own.

So try things out: experiment and evolve things and if you like what you discover in your experiments, be in touch, share what you discover -- let's continue this experimental journey as partners.

However you proceed, please don't ignore the glossary: while we strive to use simple everyday language, there is a downside to this: we need to use common words in very specific and occasionally odd ways. The glossary is meant to help clarify our tools and concepts (there's also an annotated bibliography that connects you to others.

REMINDERS AS WE BEGIN:

- Get out in the world, work with many others

- Ask yourself – what area do you wish to make a difference? Find similarly minded rebels, conspirators and collaborators. Put the book to work

- The great joy of invention is that you will change your practices, habits, outcomes and ideas many times. Welcome the change. Embrace it with a pen, pencil, eraser, extra paper, scissors, and glue.
  Cut, paste, erase, remake.

- Develop and transform the workbook. If something is not quite right for your project — that is a good thing. This workbook is meant to be transformed. Treat it only as a starting point and scaffold.

- Be playful, curious, malleable, and open to wonder.

- Pause, slow down, don't immediately jump to answering the questions. Take your time, read carefully, go out into the world, engage others deeply, ask questions, and make lots of notes.

- If the question does not apply or seems wrong, revise it (if possible never truly skip a question).

- Do things in order. Things build upon things.

- *Do not focus on solutions* (this will only lead you away from innovation). If you already know where you want to end up — then there will be no innovation. Focus on the process. Let the solution reveal itself to you through the process.

- Innovation is recursive, this means that you need to go backward and repeat steps more than once. Don't see this as a setback, it is the only way forward (really sideways — which is the new forward). If something is not working go back to the point where it was, and start again.

- To get good at innovating we feel strongly that it is most helpful to apply these tools to as many aspects of your everyday life as possible. Try them at differing speeds and with differing intensities, set yourself short challenges: could you cook a meal using this process? How about design a coat?

- Repetition is an amazing teacher: make hundreds of meals and thousands of variations of your daily habits.

- Enjoy the process, don't prejudge outcomes, fall in love with what you don't yet understand, be moved by things. Laugh, care, and be curious about what changes you.

- Be in touch.

DOING INNOVATION

Here is our detailed step-by-step guide to doing the work of innovating. It is the formalized process of *How to Innovate.* It consists of introductions and questions and activities that take you through the four tasks of the Innovation Design Approach.

Answering these questions in a room on large sheets of poster paper is not innovation. What matters is that you do the activities — in the world, with others, evolving and changing as you go.

At the beginning a notebook will suffice to keep track of things — what you will need in terms of infrastructure, location, collaborators and practices will reveal themselves as you progress.

These questions and activities alone will not suffice — you will need to both customize and change things and you will need to look to other resources to go deep into certain areas of the process. Be pragmatic and inventive with the process.

Most of what one does in innovation is to probe and learn. There is much looping and repetition. The key is to understand and develop the right probes for each task and then to be changed by the activity. To be changed is not simply to be internally changed — to have new ideas, it is to change your habits, practices, techniques, tools, taskspace, environment. There needs to be a co-emergent and co-evolutionary dialog between probing and the whole of what you are up to.

This is why innovation is an adventure — the destination and the territory do not exist before you set off.

task one

engage

"as we begin so shall we go"

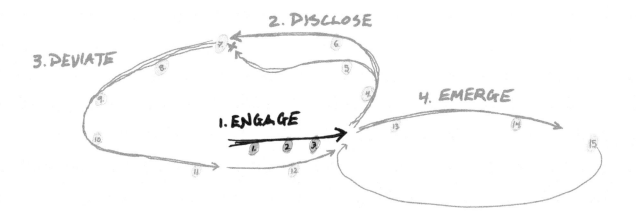

Beginning of the Innovation journey — this is the start of the adventure. On to the first task: Engage

Engagement is about being open to what can affect you. It is about being open to change, being open to the world and forces beyond what you know or might even comprehend. Innovation is not about imposing your vision upon the world. Innovation is about going beyond the known — it is about imagining that a new and totally unique way of being is possible.

To engage is fundamental to everything. There is nothing that is not always fully and totally the outcome of engagement. Emergence, systems design, probing, affordances, and exaptives — only come out from the middle of considered and deeply engaged action. Without doing and engaging nothing new can happen — only the old can reinforce itself. Everything is interdependent, emerges in action, and is the outcome of a web of complex forces. Thus innovation begins in the middle, and returns to the middle.

Too often we forget this, too often we have been taught otherwise. Many of our innovation models highlight the opposite: reflect, brainstorm, develop a plan or solution divorced from the world and others while sequestered in an office or studio. For perplexing reasons it is imagined that most of what matters can be treated separately from a real entanglement with history, community, and the environment.

Engagement is about others, it is about community — both human communities and non-human communities. All innovation design work is collective and col-laborative. When we begin the design process we are making a shared space of possibility — a type of "commons", with others. This "proto-commons" is what will sustain and nurture the design process. Ideally one of the lasting outcomes of great design is the production of a new form of commons that allows new modes of being alive to flourish collectively (this is critical to genuine worldmaking).

Engage is also about the unintended — be on the lookout for the odd — It is important to always keep one eye focused on exaptive possibilities, even at this early stage in the process.

While it is OK, and even important, at the beginning of the process to believe you have a great idea that does something meaningful — don't confuse this "solution" with the "problem". And just as importantly don't confuse this "problem" with reality. Innovation requires, ironically, you to step back, reconsider the "problem" or question, and open yourself to what is beyond the known. Real innovation begins when you let go of existing solutions *and problems*, and believe that new problems and new worlds are possible. The philosopher Gilles Deleuze says it well "A solution always has the truth it deserves according to the problem to which it is a response."

Engage involves "making to put aside": we often see many innovators — especially entrepreneurs who start the innovation journey with a clear product idea that they believe is perfect and will change the world. There is not much more to say at this point that we haven't already said about how innovation is never a linear process, or the innovation paradox and the problem with ideas. If you have a realizable concept — make it. Make it to grow with it and through it to something else, welcome what comes next. We call this part of the task of Engage "making to put aside".

Slow down, become deeply curious, have an idea and join the world — and then be moved and changed. Engage in the issue, see what others do, see what matters to others, collaborate fully. And while we call Engage a phase of the design process it is also something that you never stop doing — it will just take on differing forms as you move through the Innovation Design Process. We break the Engage phase down into three seemingly distinct stages: Opening & Grounding, Pattern Recognition, and Attuning and Gathering — while in reality it is best to blur these into one larger activity of initial engagement.

Remember, the great illusion is that we can have a view from nowhere. Design and innovation cannot afford this illusion — for it leads to many of the common problems we are faced with daily: things that solve nothing and make matters worse, or things that only made sense in the studio of the designer.

Probe, play, learn with and through the body.
Remember that most things cannot be put in words.
Be unruly. Engage immersively and transformatively in this great adventure.

SELF PREPARATION FOR IMMERSIVE ENGAGEMENT
BEFORE YOU BEGIN

Each task of Innovation requires a different mindset and approach. It is important to prepare yourself so as to be fully present in a manner that is most conducive to the goals of each phase. Here are our suggestions:

- Find collaborators and build/become part of a larger community
- Engage — fully and transformatively
- Be willing to be changed by whom you meet and what you do
- Be a participant and a good observer
- Suspend judgment
- See your biases, assumptions, and habits and bring them to light
- Be open-minded
- Learn and be changed
- Let go of your solutions and "solution thinking"
- Don't speak/assume others position
- Be willing to learn from others and the process
- Accept your ideas might be of limited value
- Embrace uncertainty & indeterminacy
- Work with others with whom you have nothing in common
- Surrender to process
- Care for your tools, practices and systems -- they are also your partners
- Develop a team: Bring those you meet into this process as part of your team for all of the phases of Innovation Design
- Understand that this is one step in a process and that you do not need to jump ahead or stay back -- Engage — participate — be subsumed — become other — make good notes — develop a team
- Be both of and alien to what you engage
- Be on the lookout for the unintended
- Build networks

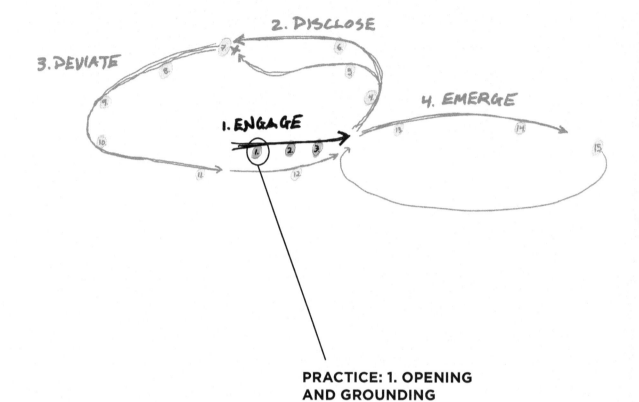

**PRACTICE: 1. OPENING
AND GROUNDING**

TASK: ENGAGE

PRACTICE: 1. OPENING AND GROUNDING

OVERVIEW

At the beginning of any creative project you need to define a starting point. This is your initial idea or hunch which relates to a direct "problem" or "issue".

Once you have defined your starting point, take a moment, describe and draw it as best you can. It is useful that you have an idea that you are passionate about, but it does not need to be a great or perfect idea — this is, after all, simply the beginning.

Once you have this: PAUSE. This is only the starting point. The goal is *not to immediately begin perfecting this idea*. To do that would be to skip over the whole process of innovation.

At this moment what innovation requires of you is that you *slow down and put your idea/solution aside* — for solutions are like answers to existing questions, and innovation requires that we become curious about the possibility of new questions, new approaches and wholly new worlds.

Paradoxically, the goal at the beginning of a creative project *is not to be creative*, but to *engage* and understand the issue and the problem — really to take a more expansive view on things in general. How does one do this? Emersion. You settle into the territory, learn, find collaborators, and are changed by engagement.

Beginning with an initial concept/solution is important because it locates you and allows you to launch into developing an immersive understanding of what is going on. Innovation begins humbly by not making huge generalizations and assumptions but by deeply engaging with people, communities and everything that makes up your area of interest. Join them, learn from them, and experimentally become one of them.

Engage is also where we begin to get hints towards unintended capacities and affordances — be on the lookout for these and keep track of these as they surface. These will often be in the vicinity of accidents,

errors, minor failures, jokes, wisecracks, asides, puns, tangential forays, etc.

Don't jump to solving anything, or creating something magical — that will come later, slow down and become of the world you are interested in. Take good notes, make good connections, find key sites and connect with potential collaborators.

Note: Often people focus far too much energy on perfecting the initial idea or having an astonishing initial idea — *where one starts is far less important than how one proceeds.* We like to quote the great innovator Sister Corita Kent:

"Begin Anywhere"

1.0 AREA OF INTREST	**What is your starting area of interest? Describe, take time to articulate fully.**

1.1 Current Approach/ Paradigm

Define the current approach to your area of interest. Be explicit about the key defining features, and the extent of this logic. Make not of key concepts, and implicit knowledge.

- Human hygiene

- As humans, we work to eradicate "germs". This is a vague term used in reference to unwanted bacteria

- Re-vamp what we consider cleanliness and hygiene

1.1 AREA OF INTREST	**What are all the different ways you could participate in this area? List and then develop experimental ways to engage.** **As your thoughts become clear, connect with others to get their sense of this area of interest.** **Get a feel for the breadth and depth of this general area of interest.**

- The current approach involves killing/removing unwanted bacteria
  ↳ Specifically the bacteria/germs that cause viruses/illness

2.0 PROBLEM Is your starting point something you wish to avoid or a problem to solve?? Describe the problem and the reasons for it being a problem.

2.0 Practices What practices should you or could you engage with to best understand this approach? (1.1)

- Test the "effectiveness" of existing hygiene products

- Understand/Research what we are looking to eradicate
    ↳ Change the purpose of the hygiene

2.1 PROBLEM Take some time to re-experience this problem first hand. Be immersive. Record thoughts on the experience. Draw. Diagraming is helpful.

2.1 Practices What did you learn from engaging with this practice in regards to how this approach (1.1) functions at an embodied level?

- Most hygiene products focusing on the same goal (i.e. hand soap, all-purpose cleaners, shampoo) tend to contain the same if not very similar ingredients. Additionally, they tend to reach the exact same results without removing the "necessary" bacteria.

3.0 MAKING   Do you have an initial concept which you wish to make? Describe

What exemplary object/tool will allow you to explore the core logic of the current approach? Describe. Why will this do this?

- Microscope - constantly see the bacteria

- Something

3.1 MAKING   Could you draw some part of this? Draw

Can you make this? Make (quickly, as best you can. Now use it and have others use it). Keep track of this activity.

OR

4. QUESTION & ISSUE

What is the immediate and direct issue/question your concept or your area of interest engages?

5. ASSEMBLAGE

What is the assemblage that surrounds, supports and to some degree defines your concept or area of interest? Describe, list or diagram.

6. UNINTENDED AFFORDANCES

What unintended possibilities are already emerging? List these & connect to Practice #7 Probing toward the unintended.

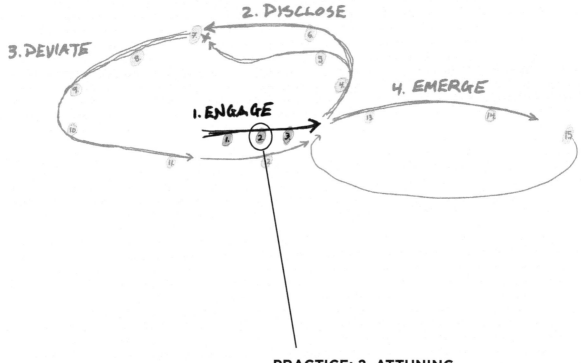

PRACTICE: 2. ATTUNING & GATHERING

TASK: A. ENGAGE

PRACTICE: 2. ATTUNING & GATHERING

OVERVIEW

You are building upon the activities and insights that are developing from the practice of Opening and Grounding. Now you are turning outward from your perspective to that of others.

In this practice of attunement — you are connecting to the broader tacit and implicit feel of your area of interest. This happens through immersive engagement with others in the mundane practices of living from the perspective of your general area of interest. You will need to decide on a location(s) and a community(ies) with which to connect.

- Cultivate care and build lasting friendships. Be changed (already) by those you meet and what you and they do together.

- Sensing and probing context and history from a subjective point of view

- A type of highly participatory immersive anthropology.

- Community building — building a future community — the community still to come

- Proto-commons building

- Wandering further afield — following some of the unintended affordances

- What are people doing? What are their concerns? What is their world?

7. DOING

What are people doing? Participate in a deep, embodied and enactive manner. As you become attuned to the rhythms (take your time), ask questions (but be equally attentive to the unspoken):

- Why are things done this way?

- What makes something well done or beautiful?

- Where does curiosity most often surface?

- Take note of the contexts of horror, dread, disgust and perplexity — how do they come into play in the general area of interest?

- Why are these things being used?

- What makes them so important/work so well?

- Have different practices been used in the past?

- Are you also using these things/processes to do other quite different things?

- What else is going on? Are there other interesting things happening that are worth following in adjacent spaces? (Go on a journey with your collaborators and partners into these spaces and activities).

- Partnering (capacity building) — forming collectives

- Sensing context and history

- Other questions/practices to consider?

8. CONCERNS

What are their concerns? Go deep with these questions — beyond the obvious

- What are people's deeper questions, concerns, purpose?
- Why does this area/activity really matter?

9. SUMMARY & CONCLUSIONS

Review collectively what you have and draw conclusions in regards to your larger area of interest.

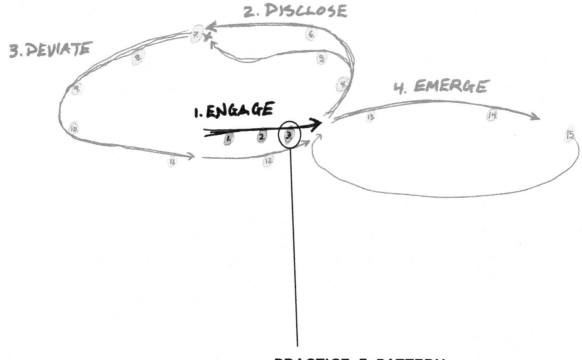

PRACTICE: 3: PATTERN RECOGNITION

TASK: A. ENGAGE

PRACTICE: 3. PATTERN RECOGNITION

OVERVIEW

This is the beginning of your shift from Engagement to Analysis. You are going from your deep immersive engagement with an area of interest to begin to develop a more general and abstract understanding of what is going on in your area of interest.

As you fill out this worksheet look back at your notes from ENGAGEMENT, these will help you immensely. This analysis begins by Seeing Patterns (this stage), and moves onto uncovering problems, approaches, paradigms and worlds in the next stage. This is a process of moving from being focused on a solution (your initial idea) to uncovering the deeper issues that this solution is engaged in. We call this "falling in love with the concern, and not the solution."

Everything has a history — a before, an elsewhere, and an after.

Begin by framing the problem that your idea "answers". Then the processes of zooming out can begin: you will sequentially answer questions to get at the big picture:

• What is the domain?

• What is its underlying purpose?

• What is its history?

• What are the trends shaping it?

• What are the big patterns that keep repeating?

• What is the matter of concern?

Note: Answering these questions requires research — both questioning users, observing what is really going on, and digging into scholarship. As such it is done collaboratively with both members of the community affected by the question/issue and those that can offer differing forms of insight (anthropologists, sociologists, philosophers, historians, etc.).

10.0 DOMAIN

An area or region. This is a question about context. You are trying to situate your idea/interest in a larger context. Additionally, you are taking a broad view to see what are all the other things that also are part of this domain.

What domain is it in?

How would you define this larger field?

Articulate the features, logics, goals and oppositions within and across this domain

10.1 DOMAIN

What is adjacent to this domain? Are there unintended possibilities here? List these & connect to Section 7 (probing toward the unintended)

11.1 WHAT EXISTS

List everything that looks like or functions like or leads to the same outcome. This is a critical step — do not do this in a cursory manner — especially if you think your design /idea/approach is exceptionally unique, for it is in this stage that you will be quickly able to see if it is or not. Most often our ideas are not as unique as we at first might imagine. If it is not as unique as hoped, don't worry, you will get there — the process will take us to truly novel outcomes. Doing this step well allows us to block what exists and push the project into genuine novelty.

What else exists? List everything that currently exists and solves the same issue/question differently

Categorize into distinct groups based upon (1) physical similarities and (2) similarities in method. Diagram each. Use color to help differentiate components.

12.0 APPROACHES

How would you define the underlying approach(es) to this domain?

12.1 APPROACHES

What are the big patterns that repeat? Diagram & try and locate your project within this diagram

13. PURPOSES

What is the larger purpose of this domain?

Why are things done this way?

What makes something well done or beautiful in this domain?

Why are these things being used (vs others)?

What is important?

14. HISTORY

When did the current approach to your area of interest begin?

How did it come about?

What was done prior?

Where does this approach not exist? Why?

15. EMERGING TRENDS & FORCES

Innovation and creativity do not exist in a vacuum, things are constantly shifting both on the micro and macro levels. Trends are the emergence of the new macro forces that have the potential to shift the entire logic of a field or culture. Research trends relevant to the larger area.

In your area of interest:

What is emerging?

What is changing?

What is stable in your area?

END OF ENGAGE

— But not the end of this process of engagement.

Take time to review, present and discuss.

Organize and summarize what has emerged.

Pay particular attention to how things have already shifted, and what unintended capacities and affordances are surfacing.

Continue to ground yourself in the context, communities, and commons.

Move forward collaboratively and experimentally.

Return to these questions, activities and your conclusions as you move through the tasks of innovation.

What you have learned in these three sub-phases or stages of Engage that will ground what you do next.

Additionally, engagement — doing is fundamental to all and any innovation activity. Stay deeply engaged.

task two

disclose

"there is absolutely no inevitability as long as there is a willingness to comtemplate what is happening"

m. mcluhan

DISCLOSURE

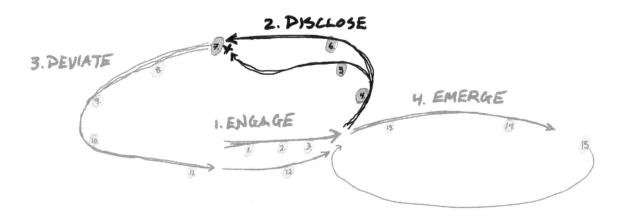

Disclosure is to go beyond the immediate understanding of things. Why do this? It is not simply for the sake of knowledge. Disclosure allows one to understand and engage with the more fundamental logic of any situation, practice, object or concept. A richer understanding of any situation allows us to grasp what is really going on and come to a more strategic and creative response.

Disclosure begins from the realization that things don't happen on their own, the ideas we have and the questions we ask along with the solutions we propose are based in more general assumptions, frameworks, habits, patterns, and ways of being alive. If we do not disclose these logics we tend to unknowingly repeat these patterns, or miss how profound an object or a concept might be. If creativity involves not repeating — then it involves not repeating the more general logics. In this manner creativity requires a rich and nuanced critical approach to the given

Disclosure can be used in two ways for creativity:

First, to discover novel assumptions, frameworks and ways of being in new experimental objects and processes (see inner dashed line in diagram). Too often we make things to solve problems, without considering how radically novel something might be (worldblindness). This leads us to miss the true novelty and potential of what we are doing. Taking time to disclose the deeper and more far reaching novelty of any innovation is critical to both grasping and participating in its impact.

The second goal of disclosing what is really going on is to prepare for disruptive innovation. Disruptive innovation requires that we "step out of the box" and this is only possible if we really know what "box" we are in. Disclosure does this. It is about discovering the patterns that keep repeating and leading to similar outcomes. Disclosure is part anthropology and part being a sleuth: what is going on and why? Patterns lead to approaches and approaches lead to paradigms and paradigms lead to worlds, and shifting worlds lead to a disruptive innovation. Much of this — the patterns, approaches, paradigms and worlds — is invisible, tacit and very difficult to disclose. Don't be put off by this, the difficulty is part of the pleasure of disclosure. Remember, this part of the creative process is about understanding, not proposing creative alternatives (that begins in the next phase: Deviate).

Disclosure also does something else: it allows you to begin to see alternative and unintended potentials that could be the beginning of novelty. Here it is critical to remind ourselves that all disruptive innovation involves the utilization of some unintended potential. We see this in literally all major innovations: from bird wings, eyes, transistors, electricity, penicillin, the internet, the wheel — and on and on... The hard part of innovation is that it is exceedingly difficult to notice anything new as being new — we tend to see novelty as either a mistake or as something we already understand — if we notice it at all. Seeing, or better yet sensing the unintended requires the willingness to be "stupid" to put aside what we know and how we know and speculate, test, play, experiment, and putter. Ultimately it requires of us a willingness to "follow" and not lead. We follow unintended "things" without knowing where they will lead and in the process we let them change us and our world.

Thus we need to do two quite distinct and even opposite things: know deeply and follow unknowingly. This is no easy task: to know and not-know simultaneously. Go easy on yourself. Laugh a lot. Stay seriously playful.

This is why our diagram splits in two (see above). Branch #1 helps you find which box you are in, and Branch #2 helps you find unintended potentials. Remember: Disclosing well — getting to the level of revealing a world allows one to really deviate and innovate a new world.

SELF PREPARATION OF DISCLOSING

BEFORE YOU BEGIN

Each task of Innovation requires a different mindset and approach. It is important to prepare yourself so as to be fully present in a manner that is most conducive to the goals of each phase. Here are our suggestions:

Your mindset and approach needs to shift as you move from Engage to Disclose. Disclose can seem like it is all about our normal critical practices of uncovering, but it is the most paradoxical and even schizophrenic of the phases because it asks us to do two quite opposite things: (1) Disclose underlying patterns of organizing, behaving, and thinking as well as (2) to be crow-like and experimentally disclose unintended possibilities. Thus your mindset must become "critical-creative".

1. CRITICAL DISCLOSURE:

- Fall in love with the issue and not the solution
- Pause, slow down and go back — engage more
- Opening up to the field of possibilities
- Getting settled into the larger problem and what grounds it
- Interrogating and researching systems deeply
- Seeing patterns, abstract gestures, and basic operations
- Finding histories and historical ruptures
- Noticing and critically following trends
- Uncovering and abstracting
- Generalizing

2. EXAPTIVE DISCLOSURE:

- Be like a Crow (experiment beyond purpose)
- Play, putter, tinker, make, use, do
- Using without considering purpose
- Jumping fields
- Search for distant and tangential similarities (broad research)
- Welcome difference
- Attune yourself away for mental reflection and towards embodied sensing of differences
- Recognize, welcome and follow your feelings of perplexity, wonder, horror, embarrassment, and disgust -- these are emotional harbingers of difference
- Be comfortable with being unsettled
- Don't force the ambiguous and nebulous to resolve themselves
- Laugh a lot
- Follow and do not lead

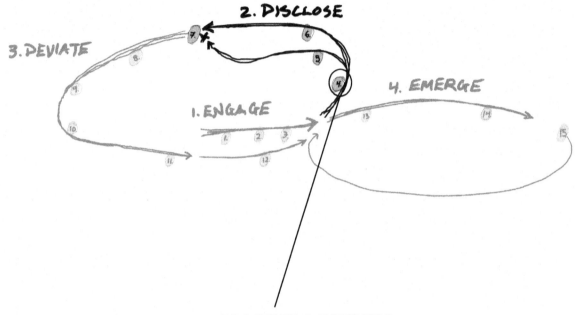

2. DISCLOSE

3. DEVIATE

1. ENGAGE

4. EMERGE

PRACTICE 4: DEFINING

TASK: B. DISCLOSE

PRACTICE: 4. DEFINING

OVERVIEW

At this point in your innovation journey it is critical to begin to separate and distinguish between the issue (the general area of interest) and what underpins it: a larger matter of concern. Why? Separating the two allows you to remove yourself from a pre-given path (the area of interest) that generates a limited field of possible problems, questions and solutions. Locating yourself in a bigger and more abstract space (the matter of concern) will allow you to co-emerge and co-evolve with a new path and develop an alternative world.

An example is helpful: you begin with a problem: *the chairs you are sitting on lead to serious back problems*. You define your area of interest: *how we "sit" to engage with work related tasks* (and how we might reinvent this). And after engaging with this in a myriad of manners you can now define your matter of concern to be: *how we connect our bodies to the environment*.

The first thing to note with our example — neither the area of interest nor the matter of concern are objective — you are making a strategic decision to frame things one way or another based upon an emerging sensibility and perspective. This can change — and often there is a need to test out multiple distinct ways of framing both your area of interest and your matter of concern.

For example, we could have defined our area of interest: *back health*, and our matter of concern: *the spine and gravity*. This would lead to a very different innovation journey. Consequently it is important to generate multiple different versions of each — especially your matter of concern.

Defining a "Matter of Concern": When we use this term the word "concern" often throws people — what are we so concerned about? It often gets understood as a "concern" that a teacher might have for a failing student. We are using in the way the Quakers used this word: a concern is something we are deeply engaged with, profoundly curious about, and comes to animate all of our activities. It is most definitely not a negative term — not a worry. Rather than worry, we should hear care, engagement and curiosity in this term "concern."

Solutions are answers to questions, and questions are ways of concretely approaching a problem. A Matter of Concern is the general area of interest of a problem or question. A Matter of Concern helps us go from the specific to the general and in doing so recognize that not only are there many ways to solve a problem — there are many, many ways to approach things. The power of getting to a general matter of concern is that we are freed up to see that not only are there many solutions and questions, but that there are many approaches. This begins to open us up to new emergent spaces of invention and novelty.

What is important to keep in mind when defining a Matter of Concern is:

It needs to be abstract

To the degree it can, it needs to distinguish itself from our general ontology and world.

It cannot be so abstract that it is meaningless (has no purchase on reality)

It should feel generative.

This is an unruly creative moment

Your "definition" will become a creative agent in the process (love it)

You can keep tweaking and transforming this

Don't forget what your matter of concern is as you move forward

16. MATTER OF CONCERN

What is the underlying "concern" that the larger domain of your issue/question/solution deals with?

Name this

Define this as carefully as possible. Be rigorous. Develop your answer from real engagement. Don't rush through this. Usually this is an inquiry into the core values of a culture.

- Now, hygiene is based on the elimination of bacteria. If the product does not provide a way to eliminate bacteria, then it is unlikely to be considered a hygiene product.

From in Class:

Matter of concern - what will not change

The care of self ← MoC

- If the product doesn't provide a way to kill or remove bacteria then it is not considered hygienic.

17. WAY OF LIFE

How does this "matter of concern" tie to a way of life?

- As of now, we know limited ways in which to get rid of bacteria without harming our skin. Therefore, most hygiene products operate in a very similar fashion with similar base ingredients

- As humans, we get rid of the "undesirables" or anything we don't want

What totally different approaches exist to your matter of concern that might be found in other cultures or historic moments?

Research (did you already come across some during the task of Engage?

Define

Connect: If possible connect as directly as possible with these. Go there. Read ethnographies. Meet people. Participate. Watch movies, etc.

- Before the understanding of bacteria and viruses, hygiene worked on a different basis

- It has always been to achieve "cleanliness" but what that means exactly changes over time

---

- Some cultures do not have the same means as us in the US. They rely on their natural bacteria to fight other bacteria instead of eliminating them both.

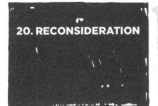

re there other ways to define your matter of concern?

List these

What are the speculative consequences of each?

Do you feel you have the "right" Matter of Concern?

Experiment, test and revise till you feel satisfied

- the definition for cleanliness ranges vastly from region to region

- Hygiene is also typically based on a group perception

Disclose — 1.) what exists
                    ↓
                 block that

2) what to follow — what takes you in new direction

Identify what you will NOT change

- Hygiene will always relate to bacteria whether we eliminate or cultivate it

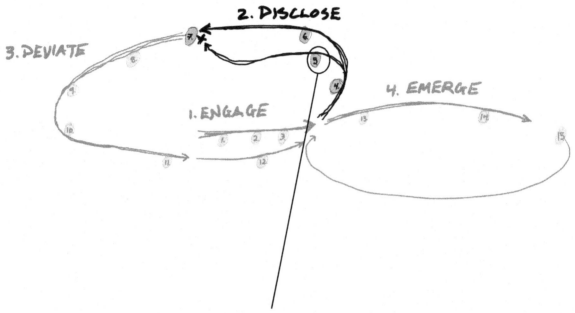

PRACTICE 5: UNCOVERING

TASK: B. DISCLOSE

PRACTICE: 5. UNCOVERING (Immanent Paradigms & Worlds)

OVERVIEW

This is the final analytical stage prior to beginning to creatively deviate from what is currently done.

It is only if this stage is done effectively that you will understand well enough the "box" that you are in — such that you can effectively "block" it, and develop a truly different mode of being alive.

Disclosing the "box" that you are in is an activity of ontological world disclosure.

To do this you are looking to understand three things:

What is the current approach that is being used?

What is the ethos/logic that underlies this approach?

What is the world that all of this fits into?

Once you understand these then in the next phase, they can be "blocked" — which will push your project into a novel and experimental terrain of possibility (the third phase: Deviate). Thus it is critical that you successfully uncover the deep logic of your area of interest: deviation is relying upon it!

To do this next section well it is critical to grasp four key concepts:

Approach: there is always a basic approach that is being taken towards an issue. This can usually be stated very simply. For example, a bar of soap has a basic approach (framework) to the question of hygiene that is "cleaning involves removing". Thus one could say that soap operates within a "cleaning = separating + removing" approach to health.

Assemblage: Nothing works alone. The assemblage is the holistic but open set of things, practices, environments, laws etc.

Ethos: underlying any approach is a set of unspoken assumptions, values, goals and habits. These need to be brought to light so that they can be put aside (via blocking).

World/Paradigm: Behind and supporting an ethos and the approach is a world or a paradigm. A paradigm is the invisible, assumed, unthought, habitual *concepts, tools and practices* that co-shape us and our most basic outlook. The paradigm could be thought of as the "mindset." Some paradigm always underlies how we understand, recognize and interact with the world. In essence: the world we have available to us because of our mode of being in the world (paradigm).

Paradigms, while complex and having many supporting components, can be stated simply. For example the "hygiene paradigm" of our bar of soap assumes that reality can be divided up into two basic categories: clean & dirty (pure & impure), and that the goal of life is to manage these (keep them apart). Paradigms always affect more than one field or issue. Again, looking at the hygiene paradigm we can see that this shapes how immigration issues, religious matters, and ecological issues are approached.

From an understanding of the approach and paradigm that lies behind and supports an idea or practice or product we can then define the "world" that this "thing" inhabits. The concept of "world" here can be understood as being synonymous with "culture" or "ontology".

Continuing our soap example, we can now ask: what is the world of "hygiene people"? What do they care about? How do they approach things? How do all the differing parts of their world fit together?

Immanence: the logic is not separate from its instantiation in practices, environments and things.

By uncovering specifically how we are always part of an assumed implicit world we can understand that our "Matter of Concern" might transcend our world and allow us a way to leave one paradigm and invent and enter into a new paradigm/world.

For innovation, defining these four concepts is critical. This next section asks you to do this. It will require research — going to the books, talking to experts, etc. These are not things one understands easily or all at once. It will take research, testing and debate.

Work on one question at a time. Write in pencil, make lots of notes, try out differing answers. Finish each question before moving onto the next.

21.0 FORM

What is the basic underlying form (shape). Describe and make an annotated drawing. Be abstract.

- Light, white, and blue items to appear "cleaner"

- Things that need to be cleaned / cleaners are typically impervious.
- Bacteria would get in if the surface was permeable

21.1 FORM

What is the general material condition? Describe.

- Soap is relatively easy to create as far as its components, but other hygiene products have to be closely monitored as their chemical formula is highly sensitive

21.2 FORM

How would you categorize (and even diagram) the basic material assemblage (organized system) that this is part of? Describe and draw/diagram

- I would categorize these materials by things that are meant to eliminate bacteria and things that are meant to give that illusion. Each category would have sub-groups.

- Its a disruption in the natural ways because of the introduction of other foreign bodies

22. APPROACH

What is the framework your concept uses to approach its area of interest?

- Since not all hygiene products truly work to eliminate germs, I think the basic logic is "do these products follow and promote the current understanding and perception of cleanliness?"

← Separate the person from the germ then kill it

23. WORLD

What is the implicit logic behind this approach/framework. Articulate the habits, tools, thought patterns and practices.

- Most products use fragrances to give the illusion of cleanliness. Others contain a lot of blue bases and dyes to "blue dye" items to give the illusion of whiter and brighter

- Our garbage just "disappears". It gets taken away
- When we think of hygiene, bacteria works the same way. We kill it or get rid of it.

23.1 ETHOS

Describe the ethos, general unspoken culture, and general values that are a critical part of this world.

- Make people believe they are killing germs and protecting themselves even if that is not the case

- Hygiene must be practiced and when it is not done in a similar fashion to what is expected, it is frowned upon

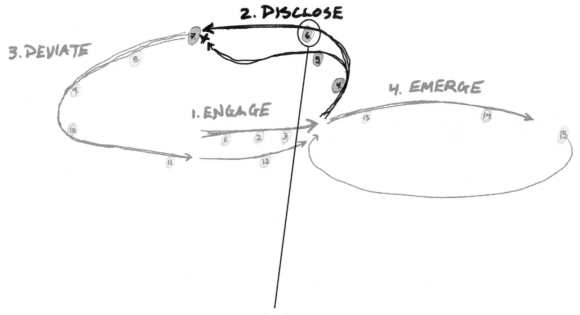

PRACTICE 6: EXPLORATION

TASK: B. DISCLOSE

ACTIVITY: 6. EXPLORATION (towards the unintended)

PROBING TOWARDS UNINTENDED POTENTIALS

OVERVIEW

There is one last stage prior to moving on to the next phase of Deviation. This is a deeply rewarding and experimental stage in which you will probe to uncover unintended potentials.

All disruptive innovations utilize some unintended potential that is found in things, processes or systems. This can be quite simply done by the moving of something from one domain to another (while perhaps changing scale, materials and purpose). There are countless examples of this: Viagra began as a heart medicine; the Wright Brothers transposed hip steering from bikes to kites; Dinosaurs became birds in part by utilizing "wings" that evolved to keep eggs warm for the purpose of falling out of trees safely. The other way unintended purposes emerge is by finding something without purpose and utilizing it to develop new forms of purpose.

The unintended is all around us and we utilize it constantly: when we don't have a rolling pin we use a wine bottle. And in doing so we might discover additional possibilities — perhaps a one-handed rolling pin (the wine bottle) is "better" at certain things? Other examples: the empty swimming pool was the first skateboarding bowl, Velcro was discovered by looking at seeds stuck in socks. This list is literally endless and encompasses all innovation.

It is worth returning to our earlier list of the differing forms of the unintended:

Intentional Components with unintended but existing effects

Intentional Components that no longer have a use

Unintentional Components that are physical by-products

Unintentional Components that are chance by-products

Unintentional Components working in category

Unintentional *Components working across category*

Begin by reviewing the answers and research you have already done.

Finding unintended possibilities is a key part of Disclosure. It allows us a starting place as we move forward to disrupt the existing and the known.

This process is counterintuitive, illogical, and disorienting to many — for we are trained to be idea generators and to trust in what can be known via concepts. But as we explained in the introduction the genuinely new is at first wholly unconceptualizable and is available to us only in action via vague hunches.

Take your time. Test things — start with your ideas and objects: play and tinker with them: what unintended potentials do they have? Are there other things in the world related to these potentials? Play. Mess around. Break things. Use things in entirely strange and nonsensical ways — invent new practices and habits. Research how others might be approaching things (don't limit yourself to our culture, this historical moment or any specific facts — speculate far and wide).

Ultimately the unintended possibilities that you discover/co-create *do not have to be complex*. In fact some of the most profound were astonishingly simple: Jackson Pollock changed art by embracing and following the unintended power of the paint drip. It is simply the beginning of differing. They will develop and get complex later. The key is to discover as many as possible, so that you can select the most promising. Make notes as you collect possibilities. List these and sketch their unique use.

EXAPTIVE DISCLOSURE:

Be like a Crow (experiment beyond purpose)

Play, putter, tinker, make, use, do

Using without considering purpose

Jumping fields

Search for distant and tangential similarities (broad research)

Welcome difference

Attune yourself away for mental reflection and towards embodied sensing of differences

Recognize, welcome and follow your feelings of perplexity, wonder, horror, embarrassment, and disgust -- these are emotional harbingers of difference

Be comfortable with being unsettled

Don't force the ambiguous and nebulous to resolve themselves

Laugh a lot

Follow and do not lead

24. UNINTENDED POTENTIALS: PROJECT

Return to your project and all the notes you have made. List and describe all of the unintended possibilities that emerged during this early research.

Return to your project and all the notes you have made. List and describe all of the unintended possibilities that emerged during this early research.

In class:

- What unintended thing comes from everything being removed

- Now, our bodies are weakened to bacteria because we eliminate so much of it. We don't know how to naturally fight it off

26. UNINTENDED POTENTIALS: ELSEWHERE

Return to your notes on exaptive possibilities that you have been making in parallel to this process. Are there any hints of unintended potentials in other fields? Can you poach a thing, or a process from elsewhere and repurpose it in some potentially novel manner? Do other creatures fulfil your matter of concern in a wholly different manner? Speculate and research broadly. Note: much of biomimicry follows from this question.

In class:

- Cats lick themselves to clean

- How does an ecosystem (i.e. a swamp) maintain its health

- Plants developed poisonous leaves so insects wouldn't eat them completely and the insects started to become immune

27. SYNTHESIZE & DIAGRAM

Diagram the relations between the various unintended potentials from previous questions. Use the Exaptive/ Adaptive Diagram as a rough template. Collectively speculate on what you have: make note of the "most novel" (a judgement call) connections and salient outliers. Highlight all of the most interesting, odd and novel potentials. Carry this over into the summary below.

Work with your expanding community to synthesize and summarize the previous two task around these three topics:

Matter of Concern

The care of the self

World

The hygiene world

Unintended Possibilities

- Cat licking
- What if we don't get rid of anything
- How do natural systems maintain their health

task three

deviate

"you never change things by fighting the existing reality, to change something, build a new model that makes the existing model obsolete"

b. fuller

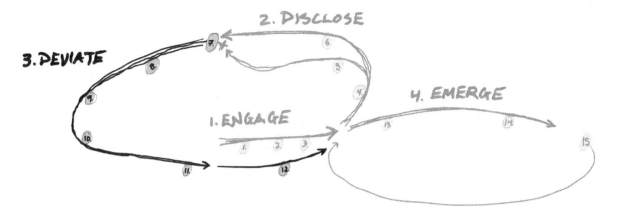

Congratulations! You have successfully moved through the second task of innovation. You have disclosed a historical mode of being-in-the-world (a world) and its unintended potentials. Now you are ready to really get creative and experimental. In this task you will be deviating from the world you disclosed so as to evolve a novel world. This is done by a two part experimental process of (1) blocking, and (2) following unintended consequences.

The goal of this process of deviation is to develop a novel world. A disruptive innovation leaves one world behind, and fosters the emergence of a new and novel world. Deviation is challenging precisely because of this — you are in a sense returning to zero. You are blocking and putting behind you the ways that things have been done, and you are setting off on an aberrant journey in which the hope is that a qualitatively new way of being emerges. Here you enter an unknowable journey — you are, as the poet Antonio Machado says, "laying down a path in walking". Your actions make the path into the future in real time.

Again, remember, you are not trying to come up with a new "product" or outcome (solution) just yet. In the final phase (Emerge) you will develop an outcome, a "product" if you will. Products are types of solutions. Solutions are answers to questions and questions are the outcome of a worldview. Thus the first thing that needs to be done is to develop a new and novel worldview.

In this phase you are developing a novel world view via refusing the framework you have disclosed and experimentally following the most promising unintended potentials in a way that lets a world emerge.

Once you have a novel world articulated, there is still one more task to accomplish in this phase and that is "mapping and relocating." A novel world by itself means little — the real question is how can this world and its worldview make a transformative impact on our current reality? We do this by mapping how they could meet, and relocating our focus of interest and experimentation to an area that seems most promising.

Review the material earlier in the book on exaptation to help you prepare for these experiments.

A word of caution and promise: this phase is by far the most challenging: knowledge and expertise are of little help — everything will become vague, nebulous and uncertain. There will be dead-ends and irresolvable paradoxes. There will be many frustrating moments when you simply fall back into the known. You will doubt yourself and what you are doing. It will make little sense when you attempt to explain things to outsiders. Have faith, trust the process and most of all trust your experiments — they will lead somewhere.

SELF PREPARATION FOR DEVIATING

BEFORE YOU BEGIN

Each task of Innovation requires a different mindset and approach. It is important to prepare yourself so as to be fully present in a manner that is most conducive to the goals of each phase. Here are our suggestions for Deviation:

Deviating is the most experimental, open and "creative" of the phases. Because of this it draws upon some of the same skills, and mental models that you needed to use during the second half of Disclose. Now you really need to push these habits even further.

- Trust the process

- Take blocking and blockages seriously

- Be open to whatever comes next — welcome whatever comes next

- Welcome difference

- Attune yourself away from mental reflection and towards embodied sensing of differences

- Recognize, welcome and follow your feelings of perplexity, wonder, horror, embarrassment, and disgust -- these are emotional harbingers of difference

- Be comfortable with being unsettled

- Don't force the ambiguous and nebulous to resolve themselves

- Play, putter, tinker, make, use, do

- Be like a crow

- Stick with the difficulty

- Laugh a lot

- Follow and do not lead

- Let events, objects and practices speak

- Make new tools, develop new habits, use new words

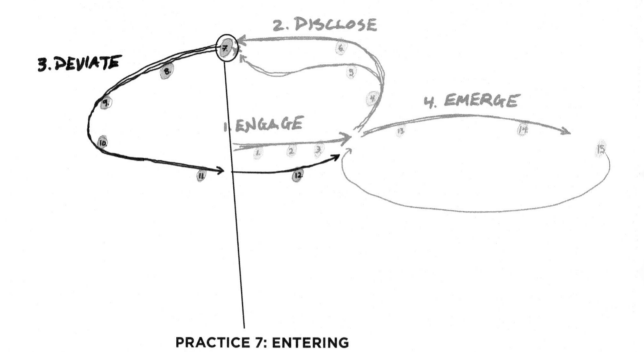

PRACTICE 7: ENTERING

TASK: C. DEVIATE

PRACTICE 7. ENTERING (defining the scope)

OVERVIEW

This is where the radically new begins. This happens via two powerful and simple operations: 1. you refuse to do what has already been done, this act we call "blocking"; and 2. you develop a new starting point based upon unintended consequences and you "follow" this away from the old and towards the new. This can be understood as a very simple formula: "Block X and Follow Y" (where X is the old logic and Y is something unintended).

1. Blocking is a critical act for creativity. All too often we imagine that creativity is about being free of all rules, this is partially true — you do want to put aside the existing rules, but the real key is to then *develop new alternative rules*. These new rules are negative (don't do what has been done) and because of this are paradoxically *enabling and catalytic*. Blocking is an enabling constraint.

Blocking relies on knowing what to block. How do you know what to block? It is what you disclosed about how things work on a deep structural level during the previous sections of Disclosure. Begin by reviewing your Disclosure work: did you really uncover the deep logic of the existing paradigm of your matter of concern? Did you fully uncover a rich and diverse set of unintended possibilities? Only when you feel confident in your answers to these questions should you proceed to this section.

Blocking is not an all or nothing operation — there is great flexibility and nuance in it. With blocking you are first deciding how deep you want to block: the more elements and the deeper you block the more novel the outcome will be. If you block simple things you will get a change-in-degree. It is only when you block more and deeper elements that you will get a change-in-kind. This is up to you.

The key in blocking is to consciously remember at every moment after this decision: *you cannot have anything to do with what you have blocked.* It needs to be a complete break. Keep track of what you have written and treat it like a contract, check what you do against it and make sure you follow it.

Remember: *it is a speculative and empowering contract:* if it leads to nothing interesting simply return to this section and change what you block and what you follow.

2. Following & Experimenting: Once you have established a block, you can now begin to deviate. Since you have blocked the standard approaches you can no longer proceed in a forward manner with your design. You will need to find a new beginning place within your world of unintended possibilities. This is what we are calling "following & experimenting" — you are following alternative (unintended) pathways & potentials and pushing them further via experiments.

Carefully answer the questions below and treat them like a starting place — your experiments in the next stage will take you further afield via a series of multiple sideways moves — don't get fixated on where you started — allow things to evolve and change (just remember not to slip back into what you have blocked) and draw from this.

Remember two things:

That these are hunches and speculations at this point. You need to put something down and try something out to see where it takes you. You cannot know in advance if it will lead anywhere. So the best policy is to trust the process and see where it takes you.

At this stage you are not trying to develop a novel solution to anything. These experiments are probes into the unknown with the goal of co-evolving and co-emerging with a novel world/paradigm.

Treat these two questions as a type of experimental "contract": for the length of the experiment you will abide by the following conditions of blocking and following.

In an ideal world you can set up multiple tests of different blockings and followings that would connect to differing definitions of the Area of Interest and the Matter of Concern.

Be speculative and inventive in developing from this "contract". Always go back and rethink both what you could block (the ontological world) and what you could follow (sense new possible unintended capacities to engage).

29.0 BLOCKING — What is the basic form to be blocked?

- Do not remove the whole of any bacteria

29.1 BLOCKING — What is the basic logic of materiality to be blocked?

- Removing/killing = clean

29.2 BLOCKING — What is the underlying approach (or aspect of an approach) to be blocked?

- Utilizing ingredients that interfere w/ our natural functions and bacteria fighting processes

29.3 BLOCKING — What world — or aspect of a world is being blocked?

- Using chemicals to kill of all bacteria

List the most promising (a speculative judgement call) unintended:

30.0 FOLLOWING   Functions

- Allowing the bacteria to exist

30.1 FOLLOWING   Processes

- Do not kill bacteria using chemicals, instead introduce different types that are able to fight off the harmful ones. Continue even if it is an endless cycle

30.2 FOLLOWING   Purposes

- Strengthen our natural fighting agents and introduce new agents to fight off more harmful types

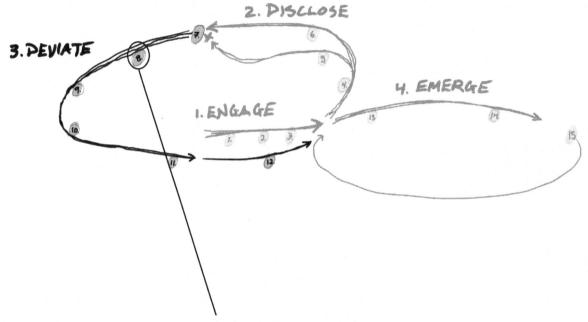

PRACTICE 8: EXPERIMENTING

TASK: C. DEVIATE

ACTIVITY: 8. EXPERIMENTING

OVERVIEW

Now it is time to experiment. The goal of this experiment is to develop a new approach to your general area of interest. It is really important to understand this:

You are not trying in this phase to develop anything like a product, and in this activity all you are working on is <u>developing a new approach</u>.

You can think of this idea of "an approach" like a "doorway" — it is just the beginning of a direction that when opened might lead to a new terrain and ideally — a new paradigm.

This phase is really difficult. There is no roadmap to the new — if there was it would not be new. It is easy to block things. Now you are creating what you do not know. You will have to rely on intuitions and hunches. Not everything you develop will lead anywhere, that's OK. Trust your collaborators. Bring in outsiders. Try out lots of things. Don't judge if things are "good" or "bad" (that will come later), right now just evaluate if they are different.

Here are some techniques we use to get started in probing experiments:

Take what you blocked, what is its opposite? Are there existing things like this in existence? In nature? What are they?

What exists outside of both what you blocked and it's opposite? What would it mean to use this as a starting point? Again, Are there existing things like this in existence? In nature? What are they?

Apply the goal of your novel world to the actual form and logic of the novel world (make form and content match). For example: the goal of a knife is to cut — can you make a knife that cuts itself?

Remember: it does not have to make sense, be realistic, you do not have to like it, nor is it a product.

Make things, do things, test things — learn from making and doing.

RULES FOR EXPERIMENTATION

EXPERIMENT AND DISCOVER THE UNINTENDED IN ACTION

- Push the unintended further — increase or decrease size, value, scale
- Be experimental — value making-thinking over ideation-creation

EXPERIMENT & CO-OPT THINGS FOR NEW PURPOSES

- Utilize the invisible & unintended
- Mix, hybridize, and mutate the unintended, the chance, the co-opted

GO SIDEWAYS RATHER THAN FORWARD

- Transpose the unintended and the co-opted into new fields and practices
- Ignore intended purpose(s)

EXPERIMENT IN A HOLISTIC MANNER

- Don't focus on one thing or scale work in a distributed and multi-scalar manner
- Develop mixes, hybrids, and mutations of the unintended, the chance, the co-opted

EXPERIMENTALLY FOLLOW ACROSS THRESHOLDS

- Follow, *perturbate, iterate and push things until thresholds are crossed and novelty emerges (a qualitative difference)
- Work in a distributed and multi-scalar manner

SPECULATE IN MAKING AT THE SCALE OF WORLDS

- In the midst of experimentation ask about the global ramifications of what you are doing as a total way of being-in-the-world
- Paradigmatically define your actions as novel frameworks and methodologies
- *Perturbation: a deviation in a system caused by an outside force.*
- *To perturbate: verb — to act on a system to cause it to deviate*

You are developing and carrying out a series of iterative experiments that follow the Exaptive Design process.

NOTE: This process repeats and co-evolves until a novel threshold is sensed. We lay this out below as three iterations — but it could be hundreds... When that threshold is sensed, then and only then is it time to move onto the next Practice: Transversal Articulation

A Note on Diagrams: Key to an experimentation for the production of unintended possibilities is an understanding of how any "thing", say water in a glass, is simply the instantiation of something (in this case H2O) under the specific forces of variables (here pressure and temperature).

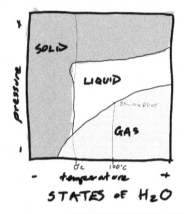

STATES OF H_2O

If you can understand that every "thing" or " event" around us is simply a particular instantiation of critical variables. And that these variables form an invisible but real field of variation. The diagram below of H2O is a very simple version of this.

Two things are key:

1. Once you know what the key variables are, you can move anywhere in this expanded field — you are not limited to experimenting with what is right in front of you. You move from seeing only the glass of water in front of you to seeing all the possibilities of liquids, gases and solids. A much larger area to explore.

2. You can change the underlying variables — then everything changes. A qualitatively new field of possibility emerges to be explored. How do you change the underlying variables? This is not simply a conceptual act: you need to change the assemblage or make a new assemblage.

In innovation there is always a relay between shifting assemblages, discovering immanent fields (via diagramming), exploring those fields and repeating this process iteratively towards the new.

The methods we use below all rely on this understanding and technique.

Diagram: Layout a terrain to experiment in using an X, Y diagram. Define three highly distinct areas of interest. Develop an experimental approach for deeply engaging each.

HW: 9

HW: 8

- Animals rolling/mud bath
- hiking/working out
- Growing yeast
- Cat licking
- Hunting
- Growing plants/seeds

Experiment #1: carry out and make meticulous notes

HW: 9

1.) Laundry
- Can't separate completely b/c we need it again

HW: 8

1.) Showering:
- Little containment Just hope that the proper things are targeted
- Killing/removal
- Focus on after feeling

Experiment #2: carry out and make meticulous notes

HW: 9

2.) Sweeping/Vacuuming
- Coincides with trash as it typically gets completely removed

HW: 8

2.) Trash
- Removal of "harmful" stuff
- Security of containers is never questioned

Experiment #3: carry out and make meticulous notes

HW: 9

3.) Brushing teeth
- Hard to separate completely but it does attempt to remove the unwanted

HW: 8

3.) Self-cleaning
- Assumption of killing
- Automatic internal adjustments made

Synthesize: review all experiments — what is most interesting and novel? What suggests a new approach? What changes the underlying variables of your diagram in an interesting and different manner

HW: 9

1.) Laundry
- Laundry just seems to have more to work with in terms of finding something novel in the end

HW: 8

- Self cleaning is the most interesting because it focuses on an internal response
- It is also similar to showering where there isn't a lot of containment

30. EXPERIMENT ITERATION #2

Review & Diagram: develop a new diagram based upon the previous round of experimentation. Layout a terrain to experiment in using an X, Y diagram. Define three highly distinct areas of interest. Develop an experimental approach for deeply engaging each.

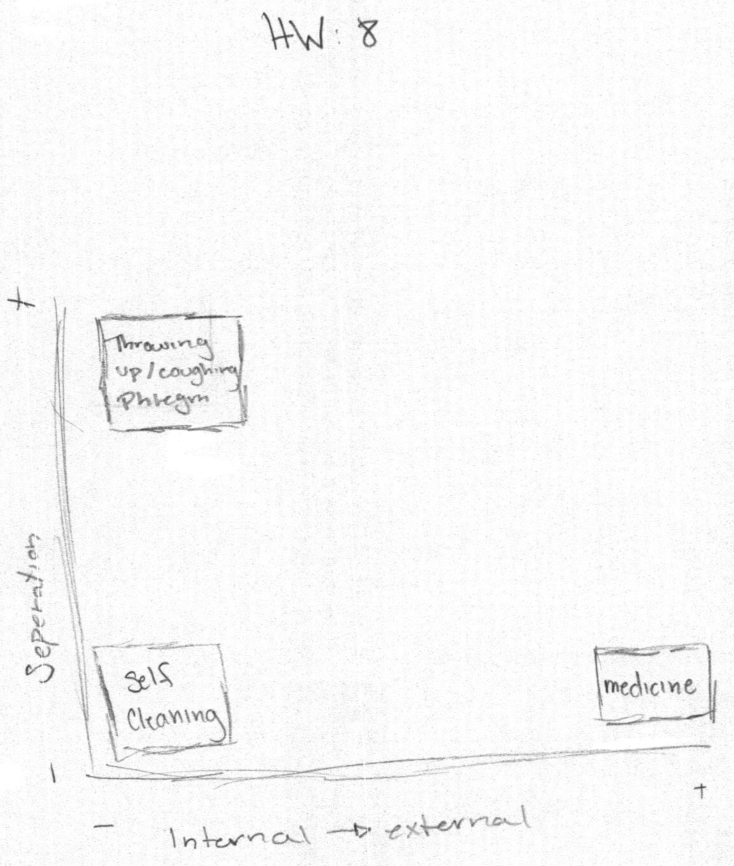

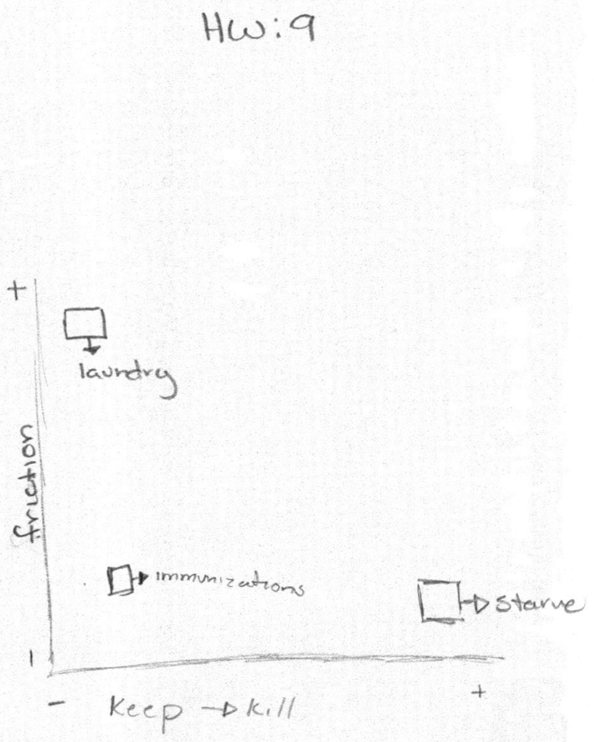

HW: 8
+
Throwing up/coughing Phlegm
Seperation
Self Cleaning
medicine
-
+
- Internal → external

HW: 9
+
laundry
friction
immunizations
Starve
-
- Keep → kill
+

Experiment #1: carry out and make meticulous notes

HW:9

1) Laundry
   - In this diagram, laundry
   is a high friction
   activity that is working
   to retain the material

HW:8

1) Medicine
   - External source that could
     interfere with natural processes
   - No seperation

Experiment #2: carry out and make meticulous notes

HW:9

2) Starve
   - In a world where everything
   is seen as living and all things
   need some sort of food, water,
   and shelter, starvation would eliminate
   germs w/out friction

HW:8

2.) Self - Cleaning
   - Cleans with internal "chemicals"
   - Relies on the body to auto
     update itself in response to
     new stimuli

Experiment #3: carry out and make meticulous notes

HW:9

3.) Immunizations
   - Recieving a flu shot or other
   immunizations don't cause a lot of
   friction and it doesn't attempt to kill
   off viruses/bacteria.

HW:8

2.) Throwing Up
   - Not applicable to all causes
     of vomiting
   - Internal components are trying
     to expel the threats to the body

Synthesize: review all experiments — what is most interesting and novel?
What suggests a new approach? What changes the underlying variables
of your diagram in an interesting and different manner

HW:9

2.) The concept of starving elements
for hygienic purposes is the most
novel in this diagram.

HW:8

- Throwing up is the most
  interesting b/c it focuses
  on the body rejecting new
  threats

- The body isn't fighting directly
  with more bacteria

31. EXPERIMENT ITERATION #3

Review & Diagram: develop a new diagram based upon the previous round of experimentation. Layout a terrain to experiment in using an x,y diagram. Define three highly distinct areas of interest. Develop an experimental approach for deeply engaging each.

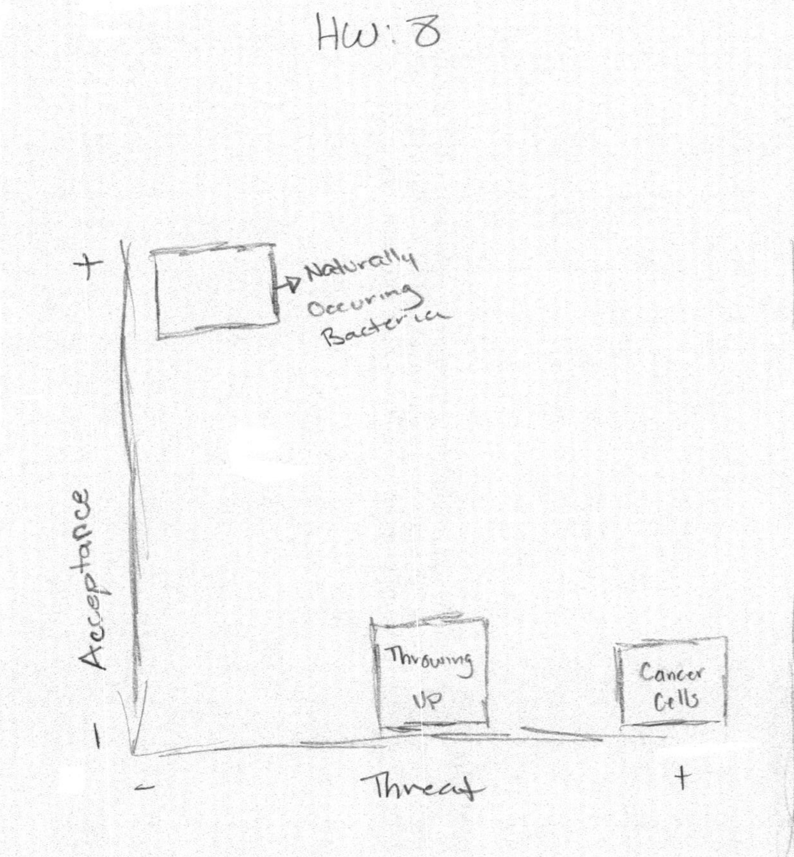

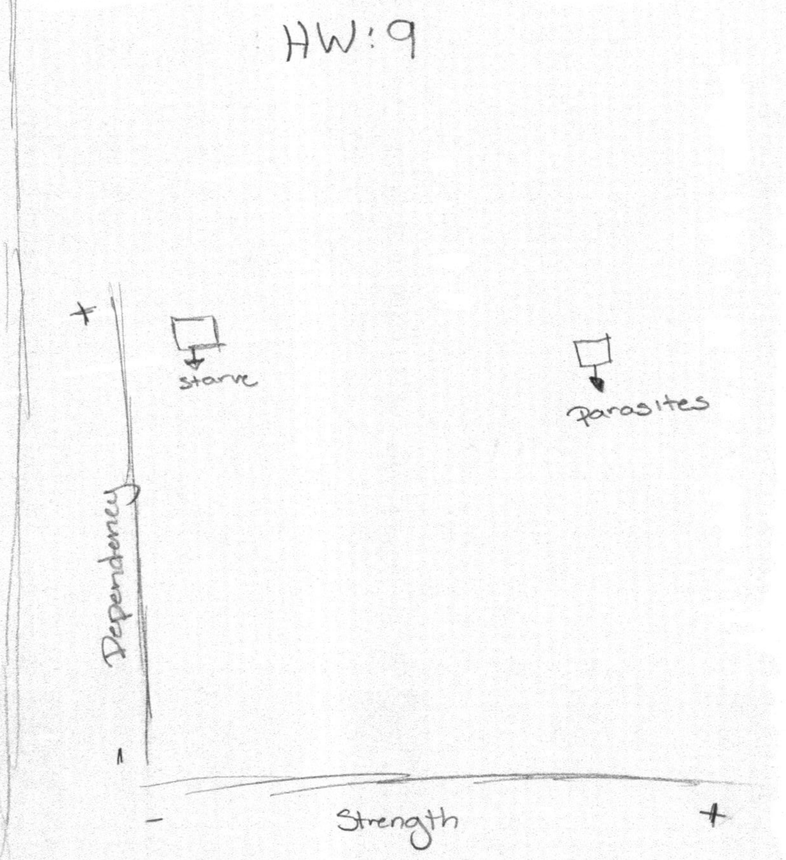

HW: 8
Naturally Occuring Bacteria
Throwing Up
Cancer Cells
Acceptance
Threat
+
-
-
+

HW: 9
Starve
Parasites
Dependency
Strength
+
-
+

Experiment #1: carry out and make meticulous notes

HW: 9

1.) Starvation

- In this diagram, "starvation" of the germs works to weaken them overall and its harmful effects on the body. It also has a high dependency on the body to grow/multiply

HW: 8

1.) Naturally Occurring "Bacteria"

- The body doesn't view it as a threat anymore, but it has adapted to now co-exist

Experiment #2: carry out and make meticulous notes

HW: 9

2.) Parasites

- parasites thrive in rough conditions making them strong within themselves, but they are highly dependent on a host to truly grow and multiply.

HW: 8

2.) Throwing Up

- Typically in response to mild threats
- The body is not accepting its current conditions.
- No adaptation to exist w/ new bacteria

Experiment #3: carry out and make meticulous notes

HW: 9

HW: 8

3.) Cancer Cells

- The body sees it as such a high threat that it can begin to attack itself as well to try to get rid of them

Synthesize: review all experiments — what is most interesting and novel? What suggests a new approach? What changes the underlying variables of your diagram in an interesting and different manner. When you reach a point in these iterations that feels paradigmatically novel and truly interesting. Really develop this as a diagram (next page), and an assemblage. This will begin the next activity.

HW: 9

2.) Parasites

- Pushing the concept of what we view as parasites to relate to a new and novel hygiene model seems to be the next stepping stone

HW: 8

Naturally Occurring

- The body can adjust itself to accept more in order to be better prepared for suspected future threats

HW: 9

Parasite

Redefine what is a parasite.
If we were solely self-serving
creatures, we would operate as
parasites to strengthen ourselves
and multiply while relying on
a host

+ Dependency —

+ Strength —

HW: 8 or 8

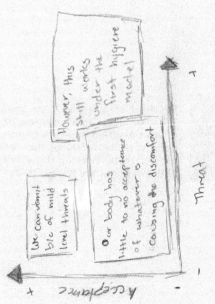

However, this
still works
under the
first hygiene
model

Our body has
little to no acceptance
of whatever is
causing the discomfort

We can vomit
b/c of mild
level threats

+ Acceptance —

Threat

HW: 9

- This world would drastically change how we as humans operate and in the long-run it would change our biology. We would need to have kids faster, have more kids, and have them be more capable at a younger age

HW: 8

- In this world, people would attempt to expel any germ that is deemed harmful from their body instead of trying to kill it.
Similar to ancient medical practices that involved removing "bad blood"

HW: 9

- As it pertains to the hygiene model, all creatures in this universe would operate as parasites. Parasites don't work to fight off what may be attacking them, instead they attempt to grow or reproduce at a faster rate. Under this model, we as humans would not be concerned w/ current hygiene ways b/c they focus containing and killing the things that attack us. Instead we would focus on growing/multiplying faster than the things that can kill us

HW: 8

- this world still follows the "separation" component of the current hygiene model which means it can be pushed even further to have no resemblance to what we currently know/do

Repeat Practice #8 multiple times until a level of genuine novelty is reached via an exaptive process

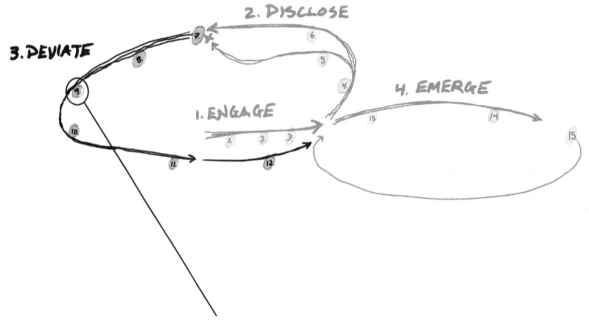

3. DEVIATE

2. DISCLOSE

1. ENGAGE

4. EMERGE

PRACTICE 9: TRANSVERSAL ARTICULATION

TASK: C. DEVIATE

PRACTICE: 9. TRANSVERSAL ARTICULATION

Being able to sense and then successfully cross thresholds (between degree and kind) is critical to the development of a disruptive innovation. As the iterations of blocking and following develop the question is always is this a meaningful/relevant threshold? Is there something different here? How can this difference be sensed and stabilized?

This practice is less a neat step in the process than a form of constant awareness and curiosity.

Additionally it is a moment of articulation — turning — that folds one back into experimentation differently — AND it draws one out of this process to bend into the next practice of Worlding.

Ultimately this is the practice of being a threshold — a portal — a step between worlds, between paradigms. Between the old and the not yet existent new.

NOTE: Please follow this model of diagramming for question/activity #33:.

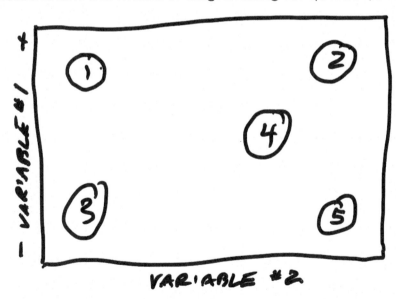

32. ARTICULATE

Take what seems like a promising exaptation. Define it abstractly as a topological terrain composed of two variables. It might take a few speculations to get the "right" variable.

33. DIAGRAM

Make a topological diagram of this exaptation using an X, Y diagram. Mark on it a set of distinct extreme points to explore. We usually recommend 5.

34. SPECULATE & EXPERIMENT

Speculate what the conditions/world is like at each point. Define and describe each of these as a separate space. Develop a set of experiments to test, engage and ultimately expand this space. Learn form the unexpected and novel (exaptive) outcomes that happen in doing the actual experiments. Do not simply ideate this. That will be pointless.

35. ITERATE

Start again with #32 and repeat a few times. At some point in this process the radical nature of your difference will be apparent. Trust this — however strange, and challenging it might be. Be prepared for the fact that in fol-

35.1 ARTICULATE

Take what seems like a promising exaptation. Define it abstractly as a topological terrain composed of two variables. It might take a few speculations to get the "right" variable.

35.2 DIAGRAM

Make a topological diagram of this exaptation using an X, Y diagram. Mark on it a set of distinct extreme points to explore. We usually recommend 5.

Speculate what the conditions/world is like at each point. Define and describe each of these as a separate space. Develop a set of experiments to test, engage and ultimately expand this space. Learn form the unexpected and novel (exaptive) outcomes that happen in doing the actual experiments. Do not simply ideate this. That will be pointless.

35. ITERATE

Start again with #32 and repeat a few times. At some point in this process the radical nature of your difference will be apparent. Trust this — however strange, and challenging it might be. Be prepared for the fact that in fol-

35.1 ARTICULATE

Take what seems like a promising exaptation. Define it abstractly as a topological terrain composed of two variables. It might take a few speculations to get the "right" variable.

35.2 DIAGRAM

Make a topological diagram of this exaptation using an X, Y diagram. Mark on it a set of distinct extreme points to explore. We usually recommend 5.

Speculate what the conditions/world is like at each point. Define and describe each of these as a separate space. Develop a set of experiments to test, engage and ultimately expand this space. Learn form the unexpected and novel (exaptive) outcomes that happen in doing the actual experiments. Do not simply ideate this. That will be pointless.

35. ITERATE

Start again with #32 and repeat a few times. At some point in this process the radical nature of your difference will be apparent. Trust this — however strange, and challenging it might be. Be prepared for the fact that in fol-

35.1 ARTICULATE

Take what seems like a promising exaptation. Define it abstractly as a topological terrain composed of two variables. It might take a few speculations to get the "right" variable.

35.2 DIAGRAM

Make a topological diagram of this exaptation using an X, Y diagram. Mark on it a set of distinct extreme points to explore. We usually recommend 5.

35.3 SPECULATE & EXPERIMENT

Speculate what the conditions/world is like at each point. Define and describe each of these as a separate space. Develop a set of experiments to test, engage and ultimately expand this space. Learn form the unexpected and novel (exaptive) outcomes that happen in doing the actual experiments. Do not simply ideate this. That will be pointless.

36. REARTICULATE

transpose the novel emergent possible paradigm into the next practice:

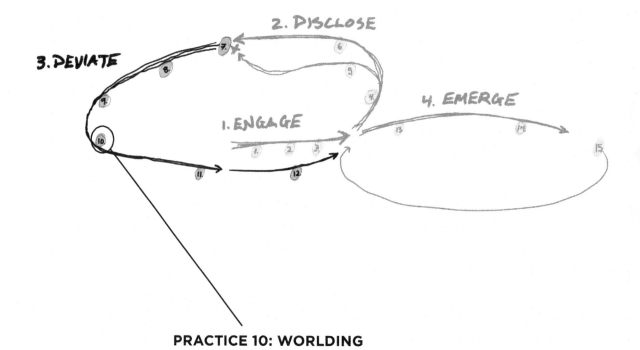

3. DEVIATE

2. DISCLOSE

1. ENGAGE

4. EMERGE

PRACTICE 10: WORLDING

TASK: C. DEVIATE

PRACTICE: 10. WORLDING

Speculative extrapolation

OVERVIEW

To develop a novel world is the heart of disruptive innovation. It is a speculative act of futurological making which has much in common with forms of fiction that project alternative histories and futures. The work of Ursula Le Guin, Kim Stanley Robinson, Octania E. Butler, Madeline Miller or Charlie Jane Anders are good examples of this speculative turn. This act of speculative world making is also found in the sciences: the works of Darwin, and Lynn Margulis are good examples. Here it's referred to as a paradigm change -- but the process is the same. What is critical at this stage is that you are proposing an alternative all-encompassing alternative approach to your matter of concern. Making a novel world is not to propose a new solution to an old problem -- it is to change the very ground rules entirely. The profound difficulty in this step is that novel worlds sound absurd and cannot be proven — they are genuinely projective speculations: this might be revolutionary, but then again it could lead to nothing. And in such a situation the tendency is to be swayed by criticism of the "devil's advocate" kind: that would never work! why would you ever want to think this way? It is important to keep these forms of criticism away (they are valuable — but only much later in the process, during the Emerge phase).

Take your most promising and different experiments and treat them like they are worlds. This is a speculative exercise. The next steps guide you through a process of turning a promising "portal" into a full fledged paradigm. The best way to approach this is to select a few of your most promising experiments and work through the questions.. It *is really important to answer the questions in the most radical manner possible* — by which we mean: you are concretely defining a world and there can be a tendency at this point to make it sound more "normal" and "reasonable" — but to do this is to lose your difference. *Keep your difference alive.*

The other thing to keep in mind as you complete this set of questions is that you are beginning to define a qualitatively different world. Keep it qualitatively different — don't evaluate it by the rules, logic, values and beauty that exist — it will have its own rules, logic, values and beauty.

Worlds, paradigms, and frameworks are best diagrammed and drawn out — words only go so far. We recommend making a (1) drawing of the world and (2) a diagram of the process that underlies your paradigm.

Sometimes it makes more sense to make a diagram of your world rather than a representational drawing. Either way, label and define all key components.

The diagram of the process is a type of flow chart. It will lay things out in a sequential manner.

Write a manifesto summarizing your values, purpose and logic. An itemized list is best. Start with the most general concepts and go to the most specific. Be clear and define terms that you are using in a unique manner.

Note: don't confuse your personal beliefs with those of your innovation. Perhaps they do overlap, but first and foremost be true to the mission of faithfully articulating the values of your innovation.

PROBES: (QUESTIONS/ACTIVITIES

37. REARTICULATION

Select and transfer/consider your most promising experiment (or simply any/each experiment). Restate it if needed.

38. DISRUPTION

What approach does it disrupt? Be both concrete and philosophical.

39. WORLD

Treat your experimental outcome as the product or exemplar of a new world. Speculatively articulate this. Draw, write fiction, diagram, get multimodal. The key is that your speculative fiction cannot lose the difference that you have developed during your experiments. Guard against falling back into existing frameworks, paradigms and worlds. It is better to be uncertain, have gaps in the story then to return to what exists and produce a known recognizable narrative. This articulation is a beginning and not an end. Name + Description:

40. DEFINING ISSUE

Considering your novel world — what would you consider its defining feature or features to be? Try to frame this as an issue or even a question. For example: the defining issue of classical Liberalism is: how small a State is needed to protect individual freedoms?

41. NEW QUESTIONS

What are all of the new creative questions that arise as a result of this world? Try and make an extensive list. Speculate on how these might play out as actual practices, logics and even infrastructures.

42. ASSEMBLAGE

What new areas of practice would be required by this world?

What experts would you need to consult? Make a list. Be as concrete as possible. Reach out to people. Talk with them. Visit labs. Bring them in for discussions. Develop research trajectories with them. Consider them part of your emerging community and commons.

43. SPECULATIVE WORLD MODEL

Develop a diagrammatic using an X, Y diagram. Try making various versions by isolating two critical underlying variables Use this diagram as a tool to speculatively explore various zones, or possibilities about your world. Make these real experiments (fold them back into the practices and processes of the previous practice (Experimentation).

44. SPECULATIVE WORLD PROCESS

Make a process diagram of how things occur in a sequential manner. Be abstract and lay out a number of possible process diagrams.

Test these by using them as instructions for action — do they lead to novel and different results?

"thought I had
reached port, but
I found myself
thrown back into
the ocean"

g. deleuze quoting g.w. leibniz

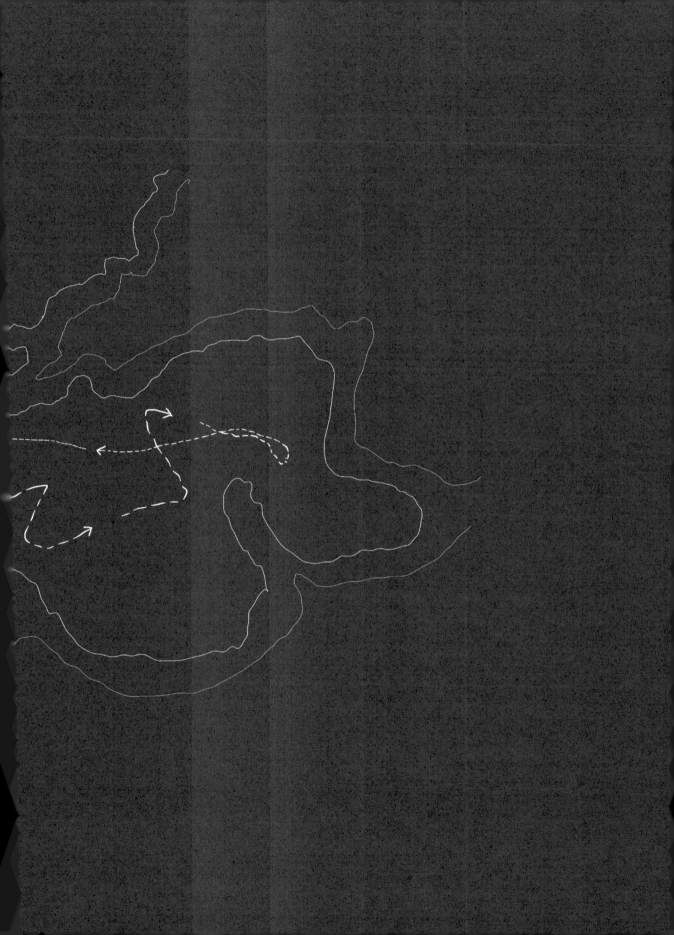

TASK: C. DEVIATE

PRACTICE: OUROBOROS: THE DEVIATION FROM THE DEVIATION

OVERVIEW

From personal experience we have found that it is profoundly difficult to develop a genuinely novel paradigm or world. Most often our first attempts still sound quite conventional and solution oriented. Because of this we developed a technique to help push a quasi-novel world into real novelty and qualitative difference. We call this the "ouroboros" technique after the famous snake that eats its tail. And true to this image, we are trying to make our world eat itself.

The technique is puzzling as it sounds: we ask of our world "how can you apply the job of the world to the form of the world itself?" This produces a paradox as an outcome — a question that cannot be rationally answered (much like a Zen Koan e.g. "what is the sound of one hand clapping?"). Answering this paradoxical riddle leads to a genuinely novel paradigm or world. And at which point we go through all the previous steps of worldmaking a second time.

This is by far the most challenging step for most people. It is very hard to leave our logic, rational problem solving and utilitarian habits behind. But the struggle is both critical and worth it — something astonishing comes from it (trust the process).

45. PARADOXICAL INFLEXION

Apply the function of your world to the world itself. This is a paradoxical and illogical task. How do you apply the action of an object to the object itself? Try it. Describe. If possible, test. What comes out of this experiment? Do it a number of times. How does this change your world (it should make a qualitative difference). Describe.

46. REWORLDING

Loop back through the previous practice of worlding. Answer all of the questions and do all of the activities. Keep doing this loop until you have developed a qualitatively distinct and interesting world

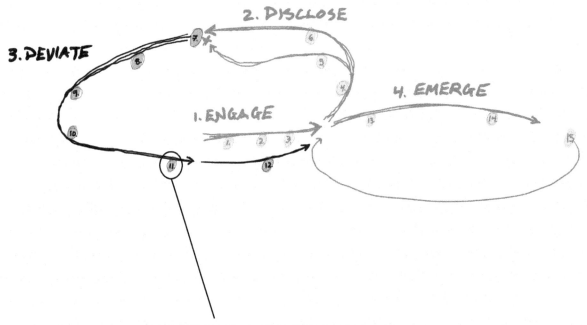

2. DISCLOSE

3. DEVIATE

1. ENGAGE

4. EMERGE

PRACTICE 11: STRATEGIC JOINING

TASK: C. DEVIATE

PRACTICE: 11. STRATEGIC JOINING

OVERVIEW

Once you have developed a powerful and unique paradigm you need to develop a way for your paradigm to meet our existing reality in such a way that it can affect a genuine transformation.

There are two directions for you to go at this point: 1. Reconnect with your original question, or 2. Follow your new paradigm in whatever you decide is the most promising direction.

To do the former is quite simple: reconnect and map the direct opportunities. The latter is a bit more involved: it requires research: how does the existing reality look from the perspective of your novel paradigm? Where is the most opportune place for your new paradigm to flourish? Where is it "needed" most? It might not be anywhere near where you originally started. This is OK, let innovation lead you. That said you can choose to keep the focus on your original "area of concern" or you can put that aside and freely follow your novel paradigm.

Take your time to do this field work. Consult experts in the fields that you listed. Ask them about your defining issue. Explain what you are up to. Learn from them. But, most of all: keep your difference alive.

These two tasks are research oriented and speculative. They are only the beginning of how your novel framework can have a concrete transformative impact on our existing world. In this way they are a transitional phase, from developing a novel paradigm/world to making it concrete.

Develop a plan to move from a novel world towards concrete outcomes. From seeing the big picture you can strategically reorient your project. This is a question that you need to keep coming back to and revising: Where and how to meet the world?

This is not a question that can be answered once and for all — it will only emerge via a long history of engagements. Very often one does practices #9-11 repeatedly until something magical happens. Play the long game. Trust the process. From here forward it is all probing, testing, speculating and seeing what emerges. Work with others, develop a community, share tools, techniques, concepts, and outcomes. This phase cannot happen alone.

PART ONE: INTERNAL ARTICULATION

47. SPECULATIVE MODEL

Develop a speculative model. Diagram and outline the practices, and assemblage.

This is not a public manifesto or argument to convince outsiders. This is a guide for the team to keep your difference alive as you progress. Write out as a series of axioms or principles. Take your time. Share widely. Pin up. Change as needed. Consider it a work in progress.

49. IMMANENT ETHICS

What new modes of being ethical are emerging from your world? Don't shoehorn your world into an existing framework of ethics, allow one to emerge. Consider the questions below as general prompts. Fold your answers back into your internal manifesto. Test these ideas out. See your immanent ethics as a powerful creative act.

In what unique way does your world empower some set of unique agents and environments?

How will your world move some set of agents and environments towards new forms of well-being?

How will your world account for its environmental footprint?

How does your world engage with difference?

How does your world engage with inequalities?

What is reality doing in relation to your novel world? Discover everything you can that might be of relevance to your novel world. Share widely. Keep your difference alive. Connect and develop your network as you do this research.

51. NOVEL APPROACHES

Write out all the key novel approaches, concepts, methods, techniques, tools, practices, environments, agents that have emerged from your world. Don't edit this list. Don't think about products or solutions — just make a massive list. Be broad and complete. And also consider going into more detail on any area that seems most promising.

52. POINTS OF IMPACT

What are all the existing fields, activities, and practices that your approach could have an impact upon?

What are all of the things that could be done in those fields, etc?

Consider specific points of impact. Do the necessary research (this can be significant). Be complete.

Consider how you are going to relate to the field that you originally began the innovation journey in. Are you concentrating on paradigmatically transforming this field? Or are you looking at other quite distinct fields? This is a significant decision and will shape the scope of how you move forward.

53. DIAGRAMMING IMPACT STRATEGIES

Develop visualization and organizational tools to understand all the connections between your novel approaches and possible points of impact. Hierarchy diagrams work well to do this.

54. RELOCATE & ENGAGE

Now you are developing a strategic plan of what to focus on. This is a big undertaking. This needs to come out of your deep engagement with the previous six questions. You will need to develop a strategy to come up with your strategy. One tool that we find extremely helpful is an Impact & Effort Matrix.

Make a blank diagram

Transfer every novel approach/point of impact to this diagram

Then edit out the three zones: Hard to find, Hard to do, and Little pay-off.

Look at all that remains along the upper edge and right side of the diagram. What is most interesting or promising?

Connect this back to other related points in the diagram.

Do these two steps for various options.

Consider each of these as possible "future backward" strategies (with the future being the upper/right edge of the diagram).

What do you have?

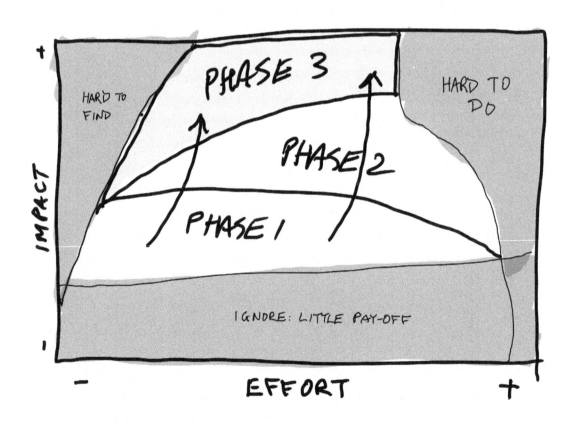

133

TASK: C. DEVIATE

PRACTICE: TEST

OVERVIEW

Testing Your Approach - The Review Presentation:

At this point in the development of your innovation it is critical to get feedback. The type of feedback you need is speculative, constructive, experimental, helps you develop the concepts, and most importantly keeps your difference alive — ideally it will help push your difference.

To get the most from feedback you need to present things in a thorough, concise manner that articulates the values, world and approach.

The other key aspect to getting great feedback is bringing in the right collaborators/strategists to review the work. You want people who know and care about the world, paradigm and values you are engaged with. Additionally you want to prepare them: *this is not a "critique" session* — it is not about evaluation (good/bad, like/dislike). You need constructive feedback that keeps your difference alive and pushes the project forward. Additionally you are looking to see if you missed something critical/creative etc.

Here is a list of what we recommend presenting:

Paradigm

What are you disrupting? (walk the group through your evolution: from the existing paradigm, to what you are blocking, to what you followed, to how this experimentally develops into your novel paradigm?)

Diagram of where it meets our current reality in an interesting manner

Choice: how you have relocated your practice

Plan: what is your general plan?

Project(s): what are the next projects/tests going to be?

Note: When presenting, take the feedback you receive very seriously and fully incorporate all of it into your plan. If you present well, in a constructive format, with the right people giving feedback — *what they offer cannot be ignored* — even if it is not what you want or expect to hear.

Use the space below to document your changed version of your project.

PROBES: (QUESTIONS/ACTIVITIES	
1. PRESENTATION	Develop your "presentation". Focus on getting people to deeply connect and understand your world. This might take you far beyond any standard presentation. Consider immersive experiences and scenarios that might be critical. Get as much feedback as possible. Utilize a really good facilitator for this.
2. REVIEW NOTES	Make considerable notes. Divide into the following categories:

World

Ethos/Ethics/Manifesto

Impact/Strategy/Opportunities

Other

3. Review Incorporation: Spend considerable time with the feedback. Share it widely with your team and network.

4. Looping Plan: Develop a plan that takes you back into the previous practices and tasks.

5. Transitioning Plan: When the project is ready, begin to move to the next task.

task four

emerge

the
encounter
makes
us

EMERGE

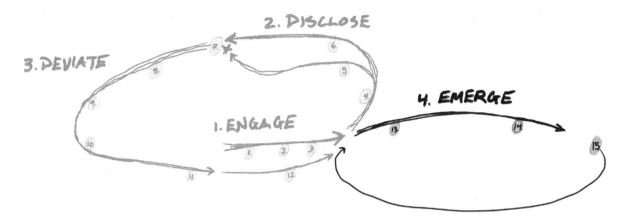

Entering the Emerge phase is not simply beginning another task in the innovation process — it involves the transition from the realm of disruptive change to the wholly distinct realm of developmental change. The world of disruptive change is one of big leaps and shifts to invent radical novelty, while the world of developmental change is all about continuity, incremental change and gradual improvement. The reason for this transition is simple: now it is time to make your speculative world real, and doing so requires entering the world of developmental change.

You and your innovation are crossing over from the universe of change-in-kind to change-in-degree and as such it is fraught with all sorts of unique difficulties. You are crossing a threshold from generating an aberrant speculative world and approach to the process of making this real enough to have a profound concrete impact. To negotiate this transition well requires a totally different set of skills and techniques than the previous phases required — and totally different skills than it will require to successfully make real world impact happen. The transition between change-in-kind and change-in-degree is its own unique activity.

Transition is a form of emergence where many distinct components align, interact and transform into a new state that is irreducible to any one component. This is a complex task where real world change happens.
The complexity is not the real challenge — that is
always there no matter what you do — the real challenge is twofold: (1) to keep your difference alive, and (2) be comfortable with the fact that this phase is just as creative and open-ended as the previous steps.
The need for creativity never ends.

Once you have negotiated the transition (stages #9 and #10) , new difficulties emerge and new skills are needed: it is time to realize some consequences of your new world *concretely* within our existing reality. This second part of the Emerge phase brings us to the sets of practices most closely associated with contemporary entrepreneurship(stages #11 through #15). This is for the simple reason that entrepreneurship focuses on fast and nimble strategies to bring things into reality. The other reason that we only now turn to these techniques is that none of the existing entrepreneurial methods have effective models for generating truly novel innovations, and thus they are best suited for working within the universe of developmental change.

Ultimately, there is no end to the ways one could approach this phase. Currently many models are taught and debated. All of these models strive to replace the classical business plan — that massive document that laid out all contingencies and planned the next five years. Such in-depth long term planning is a serious mistake from the perspective of innovation. Innovation, and all forms of new-ness, rely on open systems and emergent possibilities, long term advanced planning develops a closed linear model and as such makes innovation impos-sible. An in-depth five year plan closes off the possibility of unknowable-in-ad-vance pivots, shifts, leaps and evolutions that are fundamental to all innovation.

Techniques such as the Business Model Canvas, Disciplined Entrepreneurship, Running Lean, Design Thinking, Equity Centered Community Design and Frame-work Innovation are often used for this. Each of these has unique advantages:

Running Lean: very simple, quick process

Business Model Canvas: a strong simple iterative model

Disciplined Entrepreneurship: In depth focus on customers and connecting to customers

Design Thinking: begins by surveying users for problems

Equity Centered Community Design: powerful techniques to activate and ad-dress community

Framework Innovation: good pre design analytical tools

All of these methods stress fitting ideas/products to actual needs and users with techniques like "customer validation." What distinguishes Innovation De-sign during the Emerge phase is that outcomes *co-evolve* with the evolution of "users," environments and the makers. Which is to say all parts of the process are mutually changing each other. This is a critical distinction. The new does not come into being by being forced upon users and environments. But neither does the new leave users and communities unchanged. Each is changing the other while refusing to fall back into the old world. This process of co-emer-gence is facilitated by (1.) treating novel ideas/products as probes and not pro-totypes; and (2.) iterating on the entire process multiple times.

A final note: It is important to recognize, just because we are making something concrete does not mean that creativity stops. It takes as much creativity, for ex-ample, to figure out novel economic possibilities as it does to design any other aspect of the process.

BEFORE YOU BEGIN

Each task of Innovation requires a different mindset and approach. It is important to prepare yourself so as to be fully present in a manner that is most conducive to the goals of each phase. Here are our suggestions:

- Transitioning mindset: an awareness of leaving one world and entering another

- Become more quantitative and developmental

- Find the dynamic middle ground between novel possibilities and concrete reality

- Trust the process (go step by step)

- Understand and believe in emergence

- Engage, solicit, and foster new collaborators — build and co-emerge with community

- Have a gardening mindset: cultivation and growth

- Have a systems focus (building capacity for change, networking collaborators, feedback, etc.)

- Hold onto your novel world — rationally keep your difference alive

- Build a self-sustaining ecosystem — not a cult of your personality, or personal vision

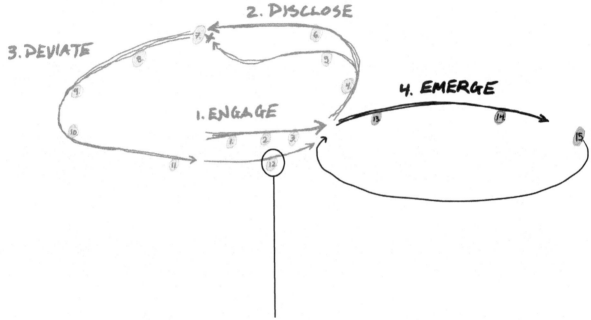

PRACTICE 12: EMERGENT TRANSITIONING

TASK: D. EMERGE

PRACTICE: 12. EMERGENT TRANSITIONING: CULTIVATING DYNAMIC CO-EMERGENCE

OVERVIEW

Whether you are starting at this phase or continuing on from the previous phase, the transition from disruptive to developmental begins by assembling and developing a network around your nascent world. The goal is to *co-evolve* what you are offering *and* a people for whom it is relevant. This might sound simple and obvious, but it is neither a one-way process nor is it black and white. You and your ideas will change and so will those who use them — you are co-evolving, small steps by small steps. If all goes well, the people you engage will transform from curious participants to collaborators, to users, to supporters, to customers. We call this "use generated design".

To do this we will do three things during this stage:

- Develop a call to engagement.

- Develop a concrete strategy to engage with communities (and why). Some of these people and communities will be experts, others potential users, and yet others are those who are super passionate about similar worlds, questions and approaches.

- Make a probe. A probe is a very simplified quickly produced tool. It should only have one key aspect or essence of what you are interested in. The purpose of this probe is to activate the field and allow interesting habits, practices, uses and trans-formations to spontaneously arise. This will require people to use and change your probe. Ideally the probe evolves in real time with many users. The probe is not your product, but what arises in these probes and tests should give you the critical insights to co-develop your product in the next stages of the process.

- Iteratively test and co-emerge (see above).

How to get good feedback when interviewing:

Get out into the world (at the right time).

Set up situations.

Document. (Photograph, video, sound, drawings, diagrams).

Take good notes.

Don't ask yes/no questions.

Take time. Figure out the right duration.

Use observation.

Let them extensively use the probe in as realistic a manner as possible.

Don't over explain, or hand-hold — let people explore and take things in their own directions.

Iterate on your interview methods. Research and test techniques. Improve.

Beware of false positives and negatives.

Note: It is important to remember that you do not have a product, and "customers" do not exist. It is critical to remember that both the "product" and the "customers" need to be co-developed — co-emerge during the process of the Emerge phase of Innovation.

PART ONE

53. INITIAL VISION STATEMENT

Your initial vision statement is a direct outgrowth of the final work that you did during the task of Deviate. Now that you have developed a specific strategy, paradigm, approach, and area of focus, you need to translate this world/paradigm into a more focused and concrete form. Now it needs to reflect how, where, and why your project is meeting a specific area of reality.

Articulate the area. Why are you different? Paint a clear picture of the new approach. Be speculative: what will happen when this approach takes place? Recognize that this statement will evolve and transform significantly

54. OPERATIONAL MANIFESTO

In parallel to your Vision Statement develop an operational manifesto — this will be a type of internal guide to keep your difference alive at an abstract level while you develop very concrete outcomes. It should remind you why your novel world matters.

55. POTENTIAL COLLABORATORS

Now that you have a new focused area of engagement, identify potential collaborators (specific individuals, communities, possible users, etc.). Be specific and make the connections, and begin to fold them into you project (see part two below).

56. TRENDS

Continue to research trends that both support and hinder your projects evolution. Do this in collaboration with your evolving network. Look beyond general trends to emerging or even forgotten technologies and practices that would be of critical importance. Fold these in.

57. MINIMUM VIABLE PROBE

At this point teams, especially entrepreneurial teams develop an MVP — a minimum viable product. This is a mistake, it is far too early for products. (Another example of what is done is a Pilot Project — also a rehearsal of the final product. But the impetus to make and get something in peoples hands is right. We like to call this a Minimum Viable Probe or a Pirate Project. The goal of this is to activate some specific environment and community to initiate a co-evolutionary process of emergence. This process will allow a community, an assemblage, and a set of tools to co-emerge. As Gilles Deleuze likes to remind us, "The foundation can never resemble what it founds ... it is of another geography, without being another world."

Minimum Viable Assemblage: What is the assemblage that is necessary for this probe/pirate project?

Location: What is the right location and group of collaborators (community). Perhaps there are several.

Test: Develop a scenario that you will use as a "test". Do a few trial runs and improve.

58. SCENARIO PLAYING

Carry out the various engagements. Understand these as scenario playing for emergent co-evolution. Make sure you have a very light hand in these engagements. What happens? What do people actually do? What emerges? What keeps happening? Pay close attention, make good notes and do not try to defend your designs or approach — let things flow and go where they go. Interview participants before and after. Engage them with your vision. What is their sense of things?

Repeat Part Two a few times with distinct scenarios that evolve and follow what emerges that is most surprising, interesting, novel and supports your world/paradigm with each iteration

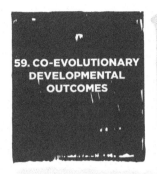

59. CO-EVOLUTIONARY DEVELOPMENTAL OUTCOMES

When the previous iterative process has co-evolved interesting results, it is time for synthesis.

What conclusions can you draw?

Should you move forward with something, or do you need to go further back in the process? And if you decide you need to go back — how far? Be open to going back to any point in the innovation journey.

If you are moving forward, the next step is to take some time to get things in order. Review and evolve your Vision Statement, Operational Manifesto, your collaborators, assemblage, etc. This happens in the next section:

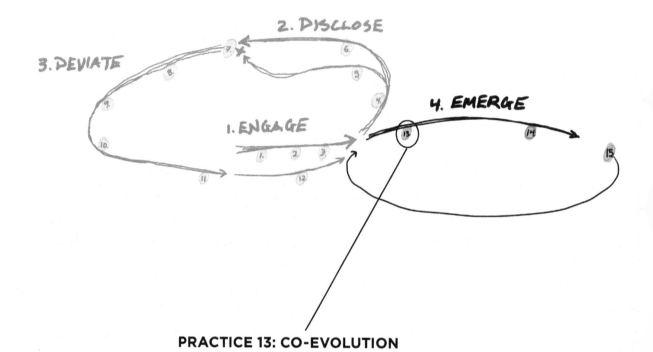

2. DISCLOSE

3. DEVIATE

1. ENGAGE

4. EMERGE

PRACTICE 13: CO-EVOLUTION

TASK: D. EMERGE

PRACTICE: 13. COEVOLUTION (& STABILIZATION)

OVERVIEW

Now, at this moment is the beginning of being more public and less protective/ sequestered with the innovation project. Up until this point you have protected your project from the everyday concerns about problems, solutions and out-comes. Co-evolution and Stabilization marks an important moment of transition.

The probes of the previous stage should have begun to evolve into a semi-stable ecosystem of engaged users, collaborators, fellow explorers, techniques, habits, tools, and environments.

Now you want to critically unpack this and learn everything you can from it. Begin by taking all the feedback and synthesize this by answering the questions "who engages." Some of these people will become key collaborators and even customers (early adaptors), but just as importantly others will be those who will feel threatened by your project. It is critical to consider what role these people/ business/interests groups will play in the evolution of your project. They cannot be ignored.

With this done, consider what you learned from the co-emergence stage. Put all of this information into the worksheet: make notes, draw and diagram as needed:

Consider carefully what you should do next in terms of your probe and research:

Do you need to develop an alternative call to action, new probes and do the process again?

Or perhaps it is a simple modification and then do the process again.

Do people connect with your world? What is really causing the connect, or the disconnect. (This might be something quite unexpected).

Remember the purpose of a probe: it is a tool for testing, feedback, change and growth. *The goal is not to simply confirm that your "product" works and "peo-ple" want it.* You are developing your concepts in a co-evolutionary manner and as such nothing happens all at once. Take your time and co-evolve. Ideally this step will loop many times. Enjoy this back and forth, take pleasure in feedback and the surprises of how others use things. We often find that the ideal number of repetitions of stage 9 and 10 are around 40! So, while learning the process you might only do this phase once or twice —in reality you will be doing it many more times.

BEFORE YOU BEGIN

Each phase of Innovation requires a different mindset and approach. It is important to prepare yourself so as to be fully present in a manner that is most conducive to the goals of each phase. Here are our suggestions:

- Become even more quantitative and developmental
- Find the dynamic middle ground between novel possibilities and concrete reality
- Trust the process (go step by step)
- Welcome more collaborators
- Understand and believe in emergence
- Cultivation and growth mindset
- Have a systems focus
- Be iterative and let the process generate outcomes
- Listen deeply and transformatively
- Be self critical
- Care about the details
- Become a competent maker
- Understand equally every aspect of your emerging business and be creative in every aspect.

PART ONE

The next step is to take some time to get things in order. Review and evolve your Vision Statement, Operational Manifesto, your collaborators, assemblage, etc. Once things are in order it is time to unpack what emerged in the Scenario Playing exercises:

60. WHO

Start by reviewing your participants:

Who are the early engages/adopters? Analyze and get specific. Develop abstract typologies. Who else would fit this? Connect. Where are they? What are they up to? What got them to be so engaged?

Who are the key collaborators? Who emerged to be critical collaborators — playing a significant creative role in what developed? Be specific. Make sure they become a part of your team and eco-system.

Opposition: Who and what became significant points of contention? Why? Was it something intrinsic to the novel paradigm or was it something about the structure of the experiment? What does this opposition mean? How can it be a constructive aspect of innovation? Test. Engage.

61. WHAT WORKED

What key components of the experiments really worked (in relation to your novel paradigm/world etc.)

Area of Interet

Benefit

Location

Novelty

Requirements

Language

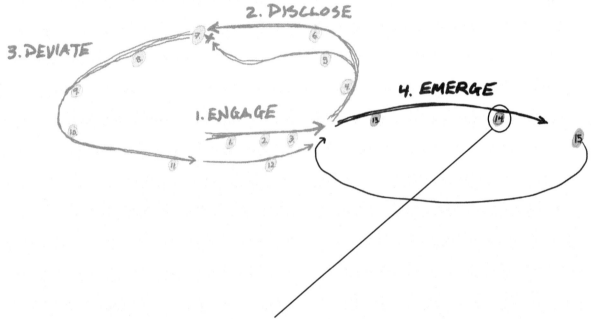

PRACTICE 14: ECOSYSTEM BUILDING

TASK: D. EMERGE

PRACTICE: 14. ECOSYSTEM BUILDING

OVERVIEW

Now it is time to move on to developing a "outcome/product" and its fit to a "need" and "market" — but only when you have a pretty evolved and stable ecosystem (users/collaborators/community, a shared worldview, practices, habits and tools)*.

This next practice begins to walk you through a series of questions to test and develop the viability of your endeavor.

*We put product, need, and market in quotes simply to note that you could, and should, define these in a very open manner.

64. DESIRABLE ITERATIONS

Focus on desirability — this is between your evolving vision statement + product and "customers". These customers should have initially co-emerged with your co-evolutionary process. Now you are looking to see that this can expand. Iterate to evolve this. Be specific and concrete.

65. ACHEIVABLE ITERATIONS

Can you actually carry out what is needed to make your outcome? What does that network look like? Who is making what by what means? Does this process really produce an outcome that is the one you and your world demands? Iterate to evolve this. Be specific and concrete.

66. VIABLE ITERATIONS

What is the economics of this process and outcome? How can you invent unique ways to make this viable? Iterate to evolve this. Be specific and concrete.

67. NOVEL ITERATIONS

Is all of this truly in keeping with your paradigm, world and vision? Iterate to evolve this. Be specific and concrete.

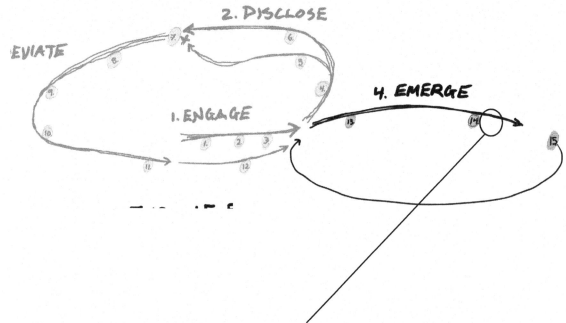

PRACTICE 14+: ENVIRONMENT BUILDING

ENVIRONMENT BUILDING PT 2: USE GENERATED ECOSYSTEM EVOLUTION
OVERVIEW

When designing an outcome — whatever form it takes (physical object, a service, an app, a restaurant, a social movement) it is critical to begin the design process in such a way as to evolve your design directly with users. The design is generative. The "use generated design" process is counter-intuitive — you are not trying to put the perfect product out there and see if customers love it, rather you are giving users the simplest version of your idea that has only one key feature (this is often called an MVP, or Minimum Viable Product). The idea is to get transformative design feedback from the very beginning of the process. The generative process is iterative — each MVP generates design outcomes that leads to the next MVP, that leads to the next and so on. This is a process of growing your design with users and will take on average dozens of rounds of iteration. This might seem like a painful waste of time that would be better spent perfecting the design away from prying eyes and criticism and only then presenting it to the world.

Note: Starting from your prototype and the feedback you have gotten from it, design the next version of your product (remember this could be anything from a service, a movement, or an object). It is really important to keep iterating and making multiple distinct products. Your mindset for innovation at this point in the process should still be one where you are "in love with the problem and not the solution". There will always be more than one physical way to solve or address any questions. Make sure you are always open to diverse possibilities as you make.

68. OUTCOME EVOLUTION

Develop and put in place an ever more actual user generated design process. Focus on Things, Practices, Taskspace, Greater Assemblage

Iterate and evolve/grow the total ecosystem.
This should be the "launch" and the beginning of the actual life of your outcome.

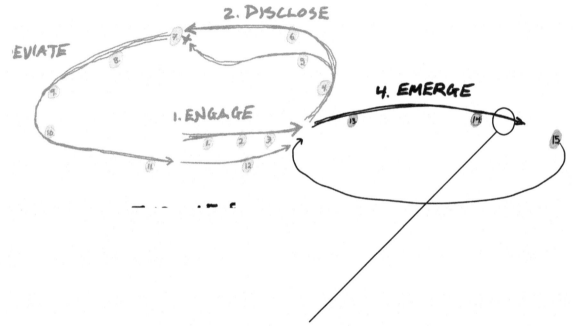

2. DISCLOSE

EVIATE

4. EMERGE

1. ENGAGE

PRACTICE 14+: ENVIRONMENT BUILDING

ENVIRONMENT BUILDING PT. 3: DEEP ITERATION
OVERVIEW

Now that you have worked through most of the Emerge Phase and developed an outcome, it is time to test this against your original ideas that came out of the Deviate Phase. This is a critical step where we can ask:

A. Novelty: Did I keep my novelty alive? Is it still a difference that makes a difference? Is this project really pushing my novel paradigm?

B. Fit: Is this outcome the best way to help the paradigm meet this reality? Is this outcome working? Should we try another possibility we mapped out?

C. New Novelty: Has my outcome done something different? Is my outcome developing a new distinct novel world? How do I take into account this new world? Do I need to map this out to not be blind to the new possibilities? Is this new novel world more interesting, or an advance upon the previous world?

Define and Explore: Take what you have done and test it against your world: go back to your paradigm and your mapping of how it meets contemporary reality. Be open to the real possibility that you need to rethink the outcome of the BMC/Emerge process.

Rethinking your outcome is a wonderful and necessary opportunity — it simply means going back through the steps of the Emerge Phase with a new speculative approach. Ideally, you would have the time and resources to take many approaches through this process in parallel prior to deciding with which to go forward.

Do this review in a similar manner to the previous review: Outside reviewers, formal presentation, and folding feedback into project. Present:

• Your Paradigm

• Your World to Contemporary Reality Fit

• Your Plan

• Your "Product"

Ask of your reviewers to use the above questions to guide their reflections and responses.

Note: Make sure you have the right type of reviewers and they fully understand what you are asking of them.

Follow the described logic above and carry out the process in two sprints & Feed these directly into your stabilized and developing world/outcome.

| 69. DEEP ITERATION #1 | Looping back to points in Emerge |

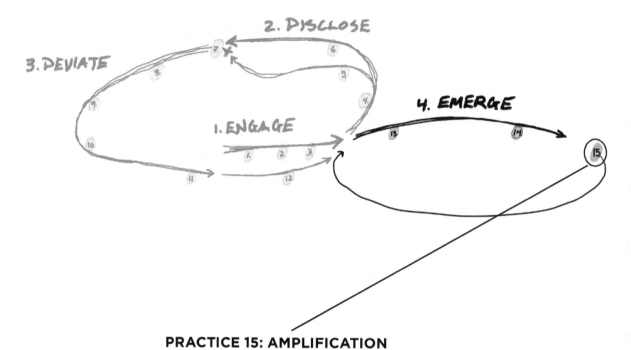

3. DEVIATE

2. DISCLOSE

1. ENGAGE

4. EMERGE

PRACTICE 15: AMPLIFICATION

TASK: EMERGE

PRACTICE: 15: AMPLIFICATION: PT. 1 ECOSYSTEMIC ROLL OUT

OVERVIEW

After doing the deep reiteration and review of your project and responding to the feedback in a concrete manner: now make a "final" version of your product. Obviously, this is no final version of your product — rather it is the "first" version of your product. It is the one that you can feel confident in releasing to the world and that can work independently of you in the manner it is intended.

Nothing exists on its own. Everything that exists only works and has meaning because it is intrinsically part of a network of other things. This ecosystem is critical to the success of your innovation — and ultimately will be your innovation. The car could only come into being with new roads, gas stations, a global infrastructure of mining (gas, metals etc.), new forms of factories, etc. The BMC is a reasonable sketch of this ecosystem, but it does not cover everything that is critical to developing a robust ecosystem.

Make a list of key components and diagram their relationships. Annotate this diagram. Determine (to the best you can) which are most critical and which might be the best opportunities. Follow up on these first. Develop.

71. FEEDING FORWARD

Develop a robust ecosystem and network

TASK: EMERGE

PRACTICE: 15. AMPLIFICATION PT. 2 REPEAT AND EVOLVE

OVERVIEW

So you think your done — this process never ends. Begin again. Return through "zero" — the unknown — the null point and begin again.

PROBES: (QUESTIONS/ACTIVITIES
Back to zero...

put
the
ladder
down

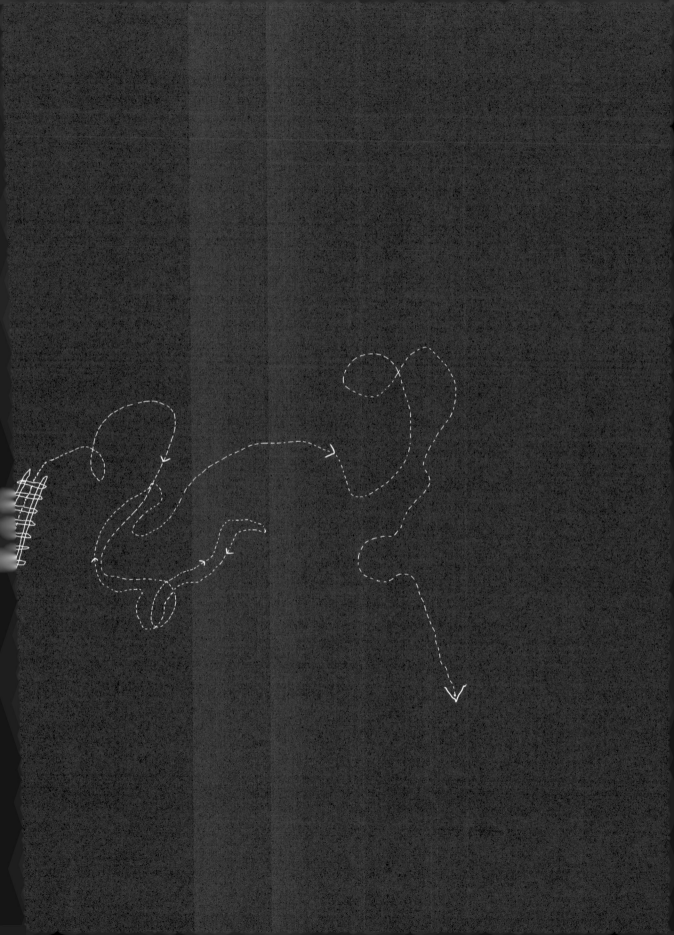

ABOUT US

Jason Frasca – Founding Partner

Jason is a native New Yorker — born and raised in the New York City metro, worked in and around every
borough, and pretty much seen everything the city
does from the back of his motorbike.

Really from birth, Jason has been an urban innovator, sleuth of futures bubbling up in the sidewalk cracks, and anthropologist of everyday lives.
Since childhood Jason has been hacking systems and imaginatively speculating on alternative futures — he likes to say that he was the family innovation consultant by the time he got to preschool. These formative
experiences led him to become an entrepreneurial
business executive, marketing, and sales
professional managing Fortune 500 and nationally
recognized clients in many diverse sectors of the
economy from direct marketing, non-profit,
entrepreneurship, startups, private investigations,
insurance, and international law. In each of these
sectors, he brought systemic and transformative
innovation that combined astute trend analysis and the right level of disruptive envisioning to push companies into blue ocean spaces.

Because of his unique approach and diverse experience midway through all of this Jason was recruited to higher ed to become part of the core faculty to invent a new entrepreneurship and innovation program.
He envisioned and brought the first maker space to a school of business and began a renaissance in how entrepreneurship, innovation, and design are taught in business schools.

From being a pioneer to now part of developing a movement to transform innovation education in
general Jason has put people, the planet, and
meaningful innovation at the heart of his approach to teaching. On almost any given day Jason can be found collaborating with colleagues deconstructing complex problems and providing a systems design approach to the collective invention of new possibilities. In his role as an academic Jason has worked on program-level curriculum development, invented new ways to teach students via intensives, international retreats,
immersive travel programs, long-term mentorship,
and transformed the infrastructure of the school.

From those rough and tumble days in New York City to the innovation consultant of today Jason has dedicated his career to designing radically innovative technology solutions and processes for companies, communities, and ecosystems with a visionary and pragmatic mindset that has yielded massive results with limited resources.

Iain Kerr – Founding Partner
Iain is a west coast kid who grew up in a very different Vancouver in an era of visionaries and dreamers.
He remembers the sailing of Greenpeace boats and summers swimming in the harbor. He spent years climbing mountains and this deep immersion in the wilderness led him to research philosophy, ecology, complexity science, and evolutionary theory and
convince him of the radical power of being generalist for innovation and creativity.

Those formative years led Iain to become a designer working at the intersection of creativity, ecology, and emergent systems — always with the goal: to make novel worlds possible. His unique approach evolves
from over twenty plus years of experimenting across and beyond the zones of Architecture, Design,
Ecology, Art, Creativity Studies, Ethnobotany, Food Studies, Systems Thinking, Social Entrepreneurship, Commons Studies and Philosophy. His focus when working as an innovation consultant is on designing novel collective processes to transform seemingly
intractable problems into, as he put it "problems
worth having for worlds worth making".
Like Jason, Iain was brought into start a new
entrepreneurship program at Montclair State University, where together they are Co-Director's of the MIX Lab (Making and Innovating for X). The MIX Lab's mission is to foster innovation at all scales.

In addition to co-directing the MIX Lab, Iain is a
co-founder of the boundary-blurring design consultancy SPURSE and the Emergent Futures Lab.

SPURSE has been at the forefront of ecological
research, experimental design, and innovation leadership for the last 15 years. While developing ground-breaking ways to probe, catalyze, disrupt and re-imagine systems both large and small, they have
collaborated with communities, organizations, and
individuals from the high arctic to inner cities
neighborhoods in Bolivia. Their award-winning
projects reveal an astonishing range of creative

solutions to effecting real change: from restaurants, wetlands, wayfinding apps, urban renewal programs, microbiology laboratories, cookbooks, buildings, everyday tools and more.

In 2018 Iain and Jason Frasca founded Emergent
Futures Lab as a platform for the rethinking of creativity, invention, and change — what they are, how they are realized, and how they can be taught. The Emergent
Futures Lab has developed a number of new tools
including the Innovation Design Approach.

Iain regularly works as a consultant, lecturer and
workshop leader on creativity, innovation, and design (MIT, Harvard University, Columbia University, Parsons, Yale, CCA, and RISD). His most recent research is on developing new models of Innovation that are collective, enactive, materially engaged forms of novel
worldmaking: Innovation Design. His and SPURSE's work has been discussed in books and journals from the NYTimes, ID, and Surface to The International Encyclopedia of Human Geography.
Now as Iain looks back from his early days hanging off a cliffs ledge to exploring the coasts of British Columbia he finds the similar adventure and joy in carrying out the work of Emergent Futures Lab internationally.

Emergent Futures Lab
A strategic innovation consulting firm.

Some refer to us as "Blue Sky" consultants. That stuffs us into a box. We don't like boxes. We prefer to tear the box up and create entirely new spaces of possibility. Because our award winning innovation program is about more than just creating product differentiation and inventing new markets.

We help make all types of innovation happen.
From co-evolving new paradigms to developing
transformative innovation cultures. We are passionate about evolving existing products and services in
unintended novel ways, and how we can use radical
innovation to meet our 21st century challenges from social to the climate crisis.

The fact is, we get fired up about one thing:
How to Innovate

Sure, we spend our free time deconstructing
innovations to understand where and why products, services and markets evolve and flourish while others wither into irrelevance. But what gets us up every
morning is working with people, communities, and
companies to innovate meaningful possibilities.

Let's connect and innovate something beautiful
together,

Iain Kerr: iain@emergentfutureslab.com
Jason Frasca: jason@emergentfutureslab.com

Want to learn more? Visit our website:
emergentfutureslab.com

Acknowledgments
This book has been many years in the making.

Over the last two decades the research and the
development of the big ideas/practices behind this project were carried out in
the field by members of the design collective SPURSE.
From there we have developed, tested and refined various models and formats
— going through countless versions for different projects and classes. Everyone
we worked with in this process, especially students and community members,
has had a critical and creative role in shaping this for the better.

Since 2017 we have been collaborating with the entrepreneurship team at the
Karl-Franzens University of Graz, Austria. Our colleagues there have had a formative hand in making this what it is.

At our academic home base: the MIX Lab @ Montclair State University, the
whole team has played many important roles. We thank each and everyone of
you — you have shaped this, and us, for the better.
Thank you.

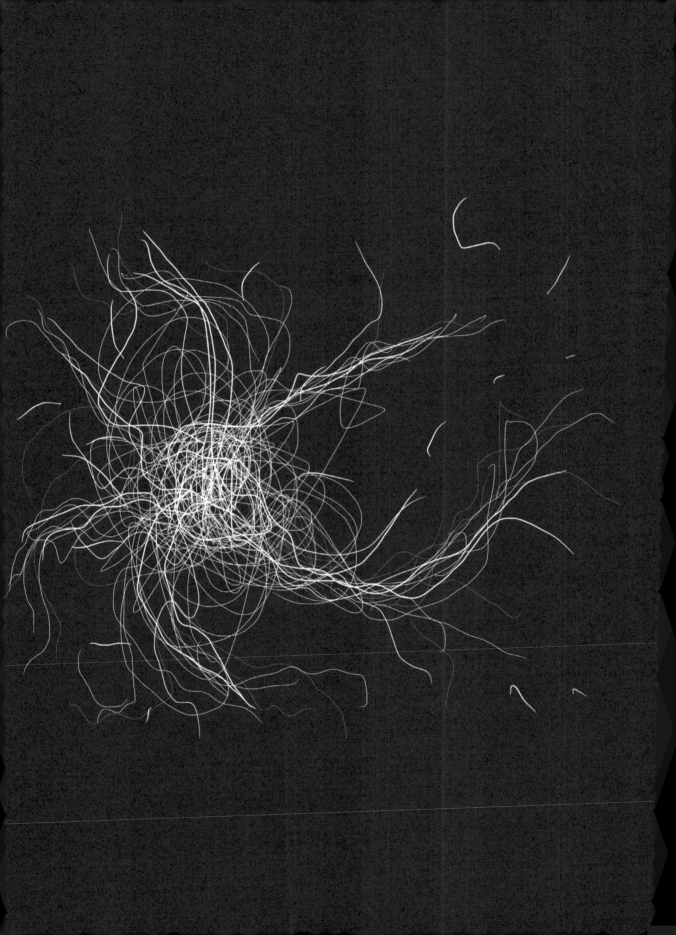

wonder
discordant
adventure
unknowable
next